STEFAN BANACH

Remarkable Life,
Brilliant Mathematics

Mathematics is the most beautiful and
the most powerful creation of the human spirit.
Only those countries that cultivate mathematics
can be strong and powerful.

Stefan Banach

Stefan Banach

STEFAN BANACH
Remarkable Life,
Brilliant Mathematics

Biographical materials edited by

Emilia Jakimowicz and Adam Miranowicz

GDAŃSK UNIVERSITY PRESS

GDAŃSK 2011

Computer (LaTeX) typesetting: Stanisław Kryszewski

Cover and Title Page Design
Andrzej Taranek

The portraits of Stefan Banach on the cover and frontispiece are from
a private collection of the Banach family

Third edition

ISBN 978-83-7326-827-2

Gdańsk University Press
81-824 Sopot, ul. Armii Krajowej 119/121, tel./fax (58) 550-91–37
http://wyd.bg.univ.gda.pl, email:wyd@bg.univ.gda.pl

Contents

A mathematician is someone who can find analogies among theorems; a better one is someone able to see analogies among proofs, and still better is one who perceives analogies among theories, and it is possible to imagine one who sees analogies among analogies.

Stefan Banach

Banach was not a mathematician of finesse; he was a mathematician of power.

Hugo Steinhaus

Banach confided to me once that ever since his youth he had been especially interested in finding proofs – that is, demonstrations of conjectures. He had a subconscious system for finding hidden paths – the hallmark of his special genius.

Stanisław Ulam

Preface

In 2005, the sixtieth anniversary of the death of Professor Stefan Banach, the Mathematics and Physics Library of Gdańsk University created a display dedicated to one of the greatest mathematicians of the twentieth century. The exhibit was presented to the Tri-city academic community in the Faculty of Mathematics, Physics and Information Science of Gdańsk University, and in the main building of the Gdańsk University of Technology.

This work originated and was compiled from the materials presented in the display and also on an Internet site (`http://banach.univ.gda.pl/`), both of which have now been supplemented with some new and previously unpublished documents and photographs.

We sincerely thank Professor Alina Filipowicz-Banach, daughter-in-law of Professor Banach, and the entire Banach family, for their support of this project, for making accessible hitherto unpublished photographs of Professor Banach, for making available the manuscript of the *Scottish Book*, and for granting permission to reproduce various materials relating to Professor Banach, including some of his publications and manuscripts, and for photographs of Banach family members.

We are deeply grateful to Mrs Maria Sowińska, the granddaughter of Maria Puchalska, for contributing an article to this publication and for permission to access photographs and documents belonging to her family.

We also sincerely thank Professor Monika Waksmundzka-Hajnos and Alicja Żuraniewska, Stefan Greczek's granddaughters, for their articles about Stefan Greczek and Stefan Banach, and for making available letters and family photographs. We very kindly thank Dr John J. Greczek, grandson of Stefan Greczek, for his recollections of his grandfather and of Stefan Banach, and for providing family photographs.

Numerous other persons provided materials and contributed in very significant ways to make this book possible. It is, therefore, with great pleasure that we now acknowledge and express our heartfelt appreciation to the following:

Professor Julian Musielak for his excellent summary of Professor Banach's most important achievements in mathematics written in a way that will make them more readily understandable for the average reader;

Professor Roman Duda for his article which reminds that the mathematical school in Wrocław created after 1945 had strong roots in prewar Lvov;

Professor Mikhailo Zarichny, the dean of the Mechanics and Mathematics Faculty at Lvov University, for granting access to the archival Stefan Banach's personal documents.

Dr Stanisław Domoradzki, Dr Zofia Pawlikowska-Brożek and Professor Mikhailo Zarichny for contributing an article to this book.

Professor Władysław Alexiewicz, Professor Tadeusz Riedl and Professor Wacław Szybalski, for their recollections of Stefan Banach, and for photographs from private collections;

Professor Marek Kordos, Dr Krzysztof Ciesielski and Dr Zdzisław Pogoda for permission to reproduce their articles;

Editorial offices of the journals *Młody Technik*, *Delta* and *Wiedza i Życie* for permission to reproduce articles first appearing in their publications;

Professor Zbigniew Ciesielski, for making available letters from the archival collections of the Institute of Mathematics of the Polish Academy of Sciences;

Charles B. Greifenstein, for sending us copies of letters from Stefan Banach and from Roman Kałuża to Stanisław Ulam from a collection in the Philadelphia Library of the American Philosophical Society, and the Society's permission to reproduce them;

The National Archives in Krakow and The Historical Museum of Krakow City for permission to access and reproduce the documents related to Stefan Banach;

Parishes of St. Nicolas and St. Szczepan in Krakow for permission to access and reproduce the copies of Stefan Banach's baptismal and marriage certificates.

Stanisław Kosiedowski for his fruitful cooperation.

Very special thanks are also due Dr John Greczek for the enormous effort he dedicated to this project and the many hours he spent translating much of the original material. The editors thank Dr Anna Markiewicz for her help in preparing the translations and Dr Wiktor Bartol and Dr Piotr Zarzycki for translations of the mathematics papers.

The editors also wish to thank Professor Stanisław Kryszewski for help in computer typesetting of this publication

Without the remarkable goodwill and support of each and every one of the above, this book, dedicated to Stefan Banach, would not have been possible. Neither would it have been possible without the fundings provided by the Rector of Gdańsk University, Professor Bernard Lammek , by Director of The Library Of the Gdańsk University and, finally, by the Faculty of Mathematics, Physics and Information Science of Gdańsk University.

Emilia Jakimowicz
Gdańsk University

Dr Adam Miranowicz
Adam Mickiewicz University

Gdańsk, June 2009.

Chapter 1

A Remarkable Life

Emilia Jakimowicz (Gdańsk)

1.1 The Early Years

Stefan Banach was born on 30 March 1892, in the St. Lazarus General Hospital in Krakow. He was the child of Stefan Greczek and Katarzyna Banach, who were not married. On 3 April 1892, he was baptized in the Roman Catholic Parish of St. Nicholas in Krakow.

As a month-old baby his parents gave him up to be cared for in the nearby countryside where he was well looked after, in exchange for payments by his father. However, after several months Katarzyna Banach took him away and entrusted him to be raised by Franciszka Płowa and her niece Maria Puchalska in Krakow [1].

Stefan Banach thus found himself in the tender care of the foster family of Franciszka Płowa,the owner of a laundry business in Krakow, and her niece Maria Puchalska. The latter's close friend and erstwhile guardian was Juliusz Mien (1842–1905). He was French but had lived in Poland since 1870 and was a man of letters, translator of Polish literary works and also a photographer. Mien was in frequent contact with his good friend Maria, her aunt and their young charge Stefan, and was the only intellectual in the boy's immediate milieu. He was, therefore, the most likely person who would have encouraged and guided his interests in mathematics and watched over his general education. It was also he who was undoubtedly responsible for Banach's excellent French that he later had the opportunity to demonstrate so well at international mathematics conferences he attended.

---

[1] See letter of Stefan Greczek to Stefan Banach in Section 2.5.

It would seem that Banach's conditions were not at all bad for the times he lived in. Franciszka Płowa's husband was the director of the Hotel Krakowski and relatively well off. Banach grew up looking on Franciszka Płowa, the owner of a successful business, as his natural grandmother and on Maria as his older sister. Nevertheless, he did not have the best memories of his childhood. He never knew his mother, although he did know and had a relatively normal, if not close, relationship with his father[2].

While under the care of Franciszka Płowa and her niece Maria, he began attending school. Not much is known about his early school days as no documents have so far been found relating to that time. However, there is considerable material connected with the time he spent in grammar school and the years that first shaped his personality and began to reveal his extraordinary talent and abilities in mathematics. He completed his primary school education in 1902 and at 10 years of age enrolled in the Henryk Sienkiewicz Grammar School IV in Krakow. It was located in Podwale Street and was commonly known by the name of *Goetz* because it was housed in a building rented from Jan Goetz-Okocimski, a Krakow brewer. The school, which emphasized the study of humanities, did not count as one of the more exclusive. However, it should be remembered that strong ties existed between the grammar schools and higher institutions of learning like the Jagiellonian University and the Polish Academy of Arts and Sciences. The staff and members of those institutions often taught at the local schools, thereby raising their academic standards. This was common practice and the norm at all of the grammar schools in Krakow.

Two of Banach's schoolmates at that time were Witold Wilkosz (1891–1941), himself a future mathematician, and Marian Albiński (1891–1978), who years later wrote his memoirs [46]. It is worthwhile to quote at length from these because they are the only source to shed light on some characteristics that Banach exhibited in those early years.

Albiński was a classmate of Banach for four years from 1902 until 1906. He then transferred to the Sobieski Grammar School for reasons that provide some insight as to the relations that existed in the schools of that time. According to Albiński the reason he transferred was due to a conflict that had arisen between him and a teacher of Greek at the school who had given him a failing grade at mid-year. In the school system at the time of the Austro-Hungarian annexation that was severely punishable by an officially recordable fine of 20 crowns.

---

[2]See Sections 2.5 and 3.1 – 3.5.

Albiński wrote as follows about Stefan Banach, and about his best friend Wilkosz [46]:

Wilkosz transferred together with me to the Sobieski Grammar School, for reasons unknown to me. Banach remained in Grammar School IV until he took and passed his final examinations there in 1910.

After I left the Goetz school my ties with Banach were not as strong as before although Wilkosz continued to maintain a close relationship with him and, as Wilkosz and I were still friends, I often saw them together.

As I remember him, Stefan Banach was mild mannered but not without a gentle sense of humor and he was a good friend at school, although a little reserved. He always wore a clean and decent school uniform, like the rest of us, and he did not look pale, sickly, or hungry, although forced through meager material circumstances to tutor younger schoolmates for money, as well as those in the wider population; his own classmates he would help freely and without payment.

From their earliest school years Banach and Wilkosz bonded together through their mutual love of mathematics. During the so-called school "breaks" I often saw them solving math problems, which seemed to me, a student of humanities, to be quite incomprehensible.

Banach's friendship with Wilkosz was not limited to only the school grounds. They would meet after class in Wilkosz's home on Zwierzyniecka Street or in the school buildings as well as in the Krakow Planty Gardens. Later on, when they were older, walking home with them through the streets of Krakow might take half the night when in a very excited state and oblivious to time they would be discussing some question or other that challenged their minds.

I took no part in these math discussions but often argued some other issues at length with Wilkosz, with whom I had a closer relationship. We were drawn together during our time at school, and even later, by a common interest in literature and a penchant for some of the same girls at the school.

After completing grammar school Wilkosz graduated with a degree in mathematics from the Jagiellonian University in Krakow where he was later to be appointed a professor.

Roman Kałuża[3] in an extensive biography [19] of Stefan Banach wrote:

There is documentary evidence that Banach was a very diligent student, which is an uncommon characteristic of geniuses. And it should be remembered that the school curricula of that time stressed Latin, Greek and modern languages, and put little importance on the exact sciences. Banach attended school when it taught precisely in such a classical tradition. Consequently, its teaching programme coincided little with Banach's abilities or interests. Those teaching mathematics

---

[3]See biographical note B-11.

were not always fully competent in that discipline and Banach in his reminiscences was quite critical of the lowly level and manner in which his favorite subject was taught at school.

A large number of documents have survived relating to Banach's second year at Grammar School IV. It is interesting to look at the syllabus for that year, and perhaps even useful to those involved with school reform:

Religion, 2 hours per week. The Old Testament.

Latin, 8 hours per week. Supplementing the knowledge acquired in the first year about regular forms and indeclinable parts of speech. The most important irregular forms. Syntax of common subordinate clauses. Verbal and memory exercises as during the first year. Every month 3 classroom assignments, 1 home assignment.

Polish, 3 hours per week. Grammar: Review of subjects covered during the first year. Complex sentences, types of subordinate clauses. Further study of punctuation and correct spelling. Reading of abstracts from literature and recitation. Essays 3 times per month alternating between home and classroom.

German, 5 hours per week. Speech in the form of questions and answers to read passages, memorizing words, phrases and whole passages. Review of regular declension and the main principles of syntax. A weekly assignment, including one per month as homework.

History and Geography, 4 hours per week. Ancient history especially of Greece and Rome employing a biographical approach. Geographical and political maps of Asia and Africa. Latitudinal and longitudinal divisions of Europe. Detailed geography of South Europe and of Great Britain. Cartographic drawing exercises.

Mathematics, 3 hours per week. Review and further study of highest common divisor and least common multiple. Systematic study of common fractions. Conversion of common fractions into decimals and vice versa. Ratios, proportions. The rule of three and use of simple proportions. Inference. Calculation of percentage.

Geometry: Axial and central symmetry, congruent triangles and their application. The most important properties of circles, quadrilaterals and polygon. Training and work assignments as in the first year.

Natural History, 2 hours per week. During the first 6 months zoology: birds, reptiles, amphibians, fish, crustaceans and worms, mollusks, protozoa. Starting in March the world of plants.

The school also offered a choice of other subjects that were not compulsory: history of the homeland, French (which according to school records no second year student selected), singing, art, calligraphy, gymnastics and stenography.

Many years later Banach said that his interest in mathematics was ultimately aroused and guided by Dr Kamil Kraft (who taught mathematics and physics at Grammar School IV).

Perhaps through overwork, or boredom with the classroom material, he lost his enthusiasm for studying. And in 1910, just before his final graduation exams, he confronted a major difficulty. He, the excellent student of former years, was now threatened with a failing grade in eight subjects! Not even the despairing math teacher may have been able to help get him through the exams (even after explaining to the high supervisory commission that they were dealing with an authentic genius in mathematics) were it not for the intervention of the school priest, Father Paweł Pyłko, who in those times would have had a deciding voice. The priest, it must be said, showed surprising tolerance in supporting the future mathematician. Banach was a skeptic and had often embarrassed the good priest with some of his comments.

Out of a total of 27 final year students 6 achieved a passing grade "with honors". Banach was not among them and had to be satisfied with a grade "with merit" (behind him were only two students who had to retake the exams).

After graduation when discussing their future plans Banach and Wilkosz were both convinced that mathematics was already so advanced that nothing new could be achieved in it; and so it would not be worthwhile to go on to study mathematics. Banach chose technology, and Wilkosz oriental languages. Much later, when already deeply involved with mathematics, Banach admitted in a conversation with Professor Andrzej Turowicz that in their youthful presumption both Wilkosz and he had been wrong about the possibility of advances in mathematics [86].

In 1910, the two friends parted company after they graduated from the grammar school.

1.2 First Great Adventure with Mathematics

Not much is known about Banach's life during the years immediately after grammar school. There is no doubt, however, as evidenced by his future achievements, that those were not wasted years for Banach. He studied mathematics on his own and for a short time attended the Jagiellonian University in Krakow.

From 1911 to 1913 he studied at the Lvov Polytechnic [76] and earned a diploma from there.

Lvov at that time was a prominent center of Polish culture and learning [77]. Those who lived there at the time were unanimous in their impression of the city as very beautiful and quite special. Of its 200,000 inhabitants, about half were Roman Catholic (mainly Polish), about a third Jewish and quite a large number were of the Greek-Orthodox faith (Ukrainian), or belonged to the Gregorian (Armenian) or Lutheran Church (mainly Austrian), as well as some other churches. It is also interesting to note that Lvov was the only city in the world where three metropolitan of the Catholic Church maintained their official seats.

Trade and commerce flourished in this conglomeration of faiths, nationalities and cultures. So did scholarship of every kind, but especially in the humanities and exact sciences, although the latter came later and was in large measure due to the work of Banach.

Aside from his studies there, not much is known about Banach's life in Lvov at that early time, about his friends, acquaintances and interests. It is likely that, as was the case in the previous and also in later years, he earned his livelihood through tutoring.

When the First World War broke out in July 1914, followed not long after by the offensive of the Russian army in response to a declaration of war by Germany, Banach left Lvov and returned to Krakow. It should be noted that he was exempted from military service because he was left-handed and had poor vision in his left eye.

Although not enrolled in any formal studies at the time, Banach continued to be passionately interested in and involved with mathematics, and deepened his knowledge of the subject through books and discussions that he often had with Otto Nikodym (1887–1974) and Witold Wilkosz, who both later became university mathematics professors.

Banach was "discovered" by Hugo Steinhaus (1887–1972), who later wrote [80]:

> *In 1916, during a summer evening while I was taking a walk in the Planty Gardens I overheard a conversation, or rather only a few words; it was so unexpected for me to hear the term* Lebesgue *integral that I approached the bench on which those speaking were sitting and made their acquaintance: they were Stefan Banach and Otto Nikodym. They told me their small group also included a third friend, Wilkosz.*

This meeting of Steinhaus and Banach had almost immediate consequences for mathematics. Steinhaus invited both Banach and Nikodym to his house and described to them some problems he had been struggling with for a long time and been unable to solve. Banach came up with a complete solution within a couple of days. It subsequently became the first of Banach's publications, written jointly with Steinhaus, titled "Sur la convergence en moyenne de séries de Fourier" (On the Mean Convergence of

Fourier Series), published in a Bulletin of the Krakow Academy of Sciences[4] in 1919. This auspicious beginning brought Banach to the attention of other mathematicians (also in no small measure due to Steinhaus).

It was a time of lively discussion among Polish intellectuals. Information flowed from many sources to inspire the learned and the scholars. Mathematics was experiencing its own important times. The very young Zygmunt Janiszewski (1888–1920) formulated a programme of work and set goals for Polish mathematics. He wanted Polish mathematics to be able to achieve an independent world standing, and suggested bringing together a number of Polish scholars in the subject and the founding of a journal dedicated solely to those branches of mathematics connected to set theory and the foundations of mathematics. He thought such a publication, published in a language more popular abroad, would have a dual role: it would make known to the world scientific community the achievements of Polish mathematicians while at the same time attracting the contributions of foreign mathematicians with similar interests. In other words, it would be an international organ for the new branch of mathematics established by Polish mathematicians. "If we want to get appropriate recognition and standing in the scientific world community, let us use our own initiative" was how Janiszewski appealed to the Warsaw community of mathematicians. This aim was very soon realized. The first volume of the periodical *Fundamenta Mathematicae* was published in 1920. Its editors were Janiszewski, Stefan Mazurkiewicz (1888–1945) and Wacław Sierpiński (1882–1969). A paper by Banach was published in it: "Sur l'équation fonctionnelle". This was notably the volume which contained the first of Banach's any publications in the new periodical. Unfortunately, an obituary appeared in the same issue announcing the death from dysentery of Janiszewski on 3 January 1920.

On 19 September 1920, Banach married Łucja Braus in St. Stephen's Church in Krakow. Łucja Braus came from a family of tradesmen. She started working while still quite young. When she met Banach she was employed as a secretary to Władysław Steinhaus (a cousin of Hugo Steinhaus) and later as a shorthand typist in the law office of attorney Lisowski. Lisowski was the son-in-law of Ignacy Steinhaus who lived in Vienna and with whose family she had been brought up until she came to Krakow. She initially spent some time in the Steinhaus family home in Jasło before taking up residence in Krakow, but continued to have a close relationship with them. Her first meeting with Banach took place in the home of Jadwiga Lisowska where the Steinhaus family was residing at the time and where

---

[4]*Bulletin International de l'Académie de Sciences de Cracovie.*

Łucja was working typing law papers for attorney Lisowski. Banach was a frequent visitor of the Steinhauses' and was interested in Łucja.

Following their wedding the couple left for Zakopane and stayed at the Villa Gerlach. Originally this had been the property of the late Dr Bronisław Chwistek which he had left to his son Leon Chwistek (1884–1944), the well-known writer and mathematician, and to his daughter Anna, wife of the accomplished mathematician, Włodzimierz Stożek (1898–1943). The villa was visited that summer by the Chwistek and Stożek families, and later by the Banach and Sierpiński families. It was there that Banach together with Sierpiński and Stożek wrote and edited their mathematics textbooks, later to be used by many generations of students [89].

In 1922, a son, Stefan Jr[5], was born.

1.3   Road to Fame

In 1920, Professor Antoni Łomnicki (1881–1941) appointed Banach to be his assistant at the Lvov Polytechnic. He did so despite the fact that Banach had not completed his university studies. This proved to be the start of Banach's brilliant career which then progressed quickly. That same year Banach submitted his original work for a doctorate at the Jan Kazimierz University in Lvov. It was published as "Sur les opérations dans les ensembles abstracts et leur application aux équations intégrales" (On Operators Defined on Abstract Sets and Their Applications to Integral Equations) in the third volume of *Fundamenta Mathematicae*.

Andrzej Turowicz (1904–1989) – a Benedictine priest and a mathematics professor who lectured at the same time as Banach at the Lvov Polytechnic recollects [86] the stories about the unusual circumstances at which Banach, a promising young scientist, obtained his PhD degree. Ciesielski and Pogoda [53] relate this event as follows:

> Not only had Banach not graduated from a university but he also obtained his Ph.D. degree in a most unconventional way. When he took up his position in Lvov he had already written several mathematics papers with important results and was constantly coming up with new ideas. However, in response to advice that he ought to soon submit his Ph.D. thesis, he would say that he had time to do so and would be able to come up with something even better compared to what he had produced so far. Finally his superiors became impatient. They had someone compile the results of Banach's latest work. It was considered to be outstanding Ph.D. material. Nonetheless, the regulations required that an official

---

[5]See biographical note B-3,

review and external examination were necessary. One day Banach was stopped in a corridor of the Jan Kazimierz University and asked: "Would you come to the Dean's office? There are some people there with questions about certain mathematical propositions that you should definitely be able to help them with". Banach went and readily answered all the questions that were put to him, all the time completely unaware that he was in front of a specially convened commission which had arrived from Warsaw for his Ph.D. examination. Most likely today it would not be possible to obtain a Ph.D. degree in this manner.

In 1922, after completing postdoctoral work, Banach was appointed a full professor at the university. Two years later he was also elected a Corresponding Member of the Polish Academy of Arts and Sciences. For the 1924/25 academic year he went to Paris on sabbatical leave to lecture and to help with work in his field that had been started there.

In addition to his heavy teaching schedule as professor in Lvov, Banach also greatly expanded his research work there. He soon became one of the greatest world experts in functional analysis of which he was one of the founders. About him he gathered several young, illustrious talents. A new institution, the Lvov School of Mathematics, came into existence under the direction of Steinhaus and Banach, and as soon as 1929 began to publish its own periodical dedicated to functional analysis: *Studia Mathematica*.

The world-wide recognition of Banach's results really came only following the publication of his book in 1931, which in the following year was translated into French as *Théorie des opérations linéaires* (Theory of Linear Operations) [3]. It was the first volume of a series of monographs titled *Mathematical Monographs*[6] of which Banach was one of the founders.

This monograph was the first textbook in the field of functional analysis and bestowed fame on both the author and on Polish mathematics.

In 1932, the Polish Mathematical Society appointed Banach as its Vice-President. His new responsibilities were quite demanding, considering the institution's standing and significance, but he accepted them without hesitation. Especially important were its publications. The renowned Polish mathematician Kazimierz Kuratowski (1896–1980), one of the original founders of the Society, appraised them as follows [21]:

The decision in 1931 to start publishing the Mathematical Monographs *should be considered a particularly important event for Polish mathematics. It marked a new stage in the development of the Polish School of Mathematics. The earliest stage, which could be called the pioneering stage, was characterized by the publication, almost always, of short articles containing new results (appearing mainly*

---

[6]*Monografie Matematyczne* (in Polish).

in Fundamenta Mathematicae and Studia Mathematica). A time came, however, for a synthesis of all of the achievements of Polish mathematicians, or even for a synthesis of all the mathematics disciplines in which Poles had made especially significant contributions. The initial plan was to publish monographs on the subject of functional analysis: Volume I Operations lineares (Theory of Linear Operations) by Banach, Volume II Théorie de l'integrale (Theory of Integral) by Saks[7], Volume III Topology by Kuratowski, Volume IV Continuum hypothesis by Sierpiński and Volume V Theory of Trigonometric Series by Steinhaus and Kaczmarz[8]. In a very short time the Mathematical Monographs achieved a position as one of the most important scientific periodicals.

Banach also wrote textbooks of advanced mathematics that were associated with and complemented his teaching programme. Thus, volumes I and II of *Differential and Integral Calculus* [2] appeared in 1929 and 1930, respectively, and volumes I and II of *Mechanics – In the Scope of Academic Studies* [4] were both published in 1938. These, as well as texts for use in grammar schools [89], co-authored with Stożek and Sierpiński, were created during somewhat dramatic circumstances for Banach. Steinhaus wrote [80]:

He was always able to work under any conditions, and in all circumstances, and was unaccustomed to ease and comfort. His professor's salary of about 1000 zlotys per month should have been quite adequate. However, his fondness for frequenting coffee-houses, utter disregard of any bourgeois concern for material interests, and an absence of regularity in daily affairs, finally plunged him into debt and very trying times. In an attempt to change his situation he began writing textbooks.

Turowicz mentions [86] that Banach received help at that time from Professor Benedykt Fuliński (1881–1942), who guaranteed his debts to the creditors. At the same time Fuliński was instrumental in getting Banach to change his spending habits and set aside some of his income every month. However, it was only his substantial income from his books that helped to pay down the debts, which were only completely liquidated when Banach received a prize from the Polish Academy of Arts and Sciences. By this time it was already 1939.

In the meantime there was extensive world-wide interest by mathematicians in Banach's work and results. At the 1936 International Congress of Mathematics in Oslo Banach was entrusted with giving one of the keynote lectures on *Die Theorie der Operationen und ihre Bedeutung für die Analysis* (The Theory of Operations and its Significance in Analysis), which was undoubtedly a sign of the high regard for and interest in him personally

---

[7]Stanisław Saks (1897–1942).
[8]Stefan Kaczmarz (1895–1940).

and in his results.

In those days guests from all over the world visited Lvov:

from Austria – Moses Jacob,
from Czechoslovakia – Vaclaw Hlavaty,
from Denmark – Axel Andersen,
from France – Emil Borel, Maurice Fréchet, Henri Lebesgue,
    Paul Montel,
from Germany – Leon Lichtenstein, Ernst Zermelo,
from Great Britain – A. Cyril Offord, A.J. Ward,
from Romania – Pierre Segrescu, Simion Stoilov,
from Switzerland Rolin Wavre,
from the USA – John von Neumann,
from the Soviet Union – Pavel S. Alexandrov, Nina Bari,
    Nikolai N. Bogolyubov, Lazar A. Lusternik, Nikolai Luzin,
    Dimitrii Menshov, S. Sobolev, and others.

in addition to the frequent visits of other Polish mathematicians, e.g.,

from Warsaw – Karol Borsuk, Stefan Mazurkiewicz,
    Alfred Tarski, Wacław Sierpiński,
from Vilnius – Antoni Zygmund.

Functional analysis was the main domain of Banach's scientific work, and his results with it brought him world fame, but he also made significant contributions in other areas of mathematics. These included his work on the theory of real functions, the theory of orthogonal series, and set theory. One of the most spectacular results of set theory was discovered jointly by Banach and Alfred Tarski (Teitelbaum) (1902–1983) and was published in the paper "Sur la décomposition des ensembles de parties respectivement congruentes" (On Dissection of Sets of Points into Equal Parts), in Volume VI of *Fundamenta Mathematicae*. In this surprising paper, written in French in 1924, the authors discovered that it is possible, by using very original operations, to decompose a ball into parts and reassemble the parts into two balls each identical to the original.

1.4 The Scottish Café

The Lvov School of Mathematics was renowned for its coffee-house life, which had always been a favourite of Banach's. In Lvov the meetings to discuss mathematics were held in coffee-houses near the Mathematics Faculty, as in the Scottish Café, on Fredro Street. Everyday sessions in the Scottish Café, near the University, were very often continuations of the meetings of the Lvov group of the Polish Mathematical Society, and became an integral part of the mathematicians' scientific work.

The students at the university did not normally frequent the Scottish Café, and only two, Stanisław Ulam[9] (1909–1984) and his friend Józef Schreier (1909–1943), were honored during their time as undergraduates to be invited to participate in meetings there and to interact with such very gifted mathematicians. Professor Andrzej Alexiewicz[10] (1917–1995) comments that to be invited to the Scottish Café was tantamount to being knighted. Banach, Ulam and Stanisław Mazur (1905–1981) formed the most intensive working team there.

One advantage of the Scottish Café was that it had marble tabletops on which one could easily write and, perhaps more importantly, from which the writing could be easily and quickly erased.

According to Hugo Steinhaus [80]:

One session lasted 17 hours and resulted in the successful proof of an important postulate concerning Banach spaces. No permanent record of it was made, however, and no one since has been able to reproduce it because it was probably completely erased from the tabletop by the cleaners. Unfortunately, many other proofs derived by Banach and his students suffered the same fate.

The many hours spent in discussion of mathematics problems resulted in an atmosphere of perseverance, excitement and concentration and made it possible to forge intellectual common ground.

Stanisław Ulam recalled [39]:

These long sessions in the cafes with Banach, or more often with Banach and Mazur, were probably unique. Collaboration was on a scale and with an intensity I have never seen surpassed, equaled or approximated anywhere – except perhaps at Los Alamos during the war years.

It would seem that for those who regularly took part in these meetings and discussions at the Scottish Café, what they were engaged in was not work but fun. It was in the end a significant achievement, therefore, by Banach's wife Łucja to have had the inspiration to buy a thick, hard covered notebook that she presented either to the cashier or barman, or perhaps to a cloak room attendant of the Scottish Café with instructions to give it to any mathematician who wanted to use it. Thus in the space of a few years

---

[9]See biographical note B-20.
[10]See biographical note B-1.

The old Jan Kazimierz University (JKU) at 4, St. Nicholas Street,
and the St. Nicholas Church - from a 1915 postcard.

The old JKU - from a contemporary photograph.

Professor Andrzej Alexiewicz participating in the ceremony
to place a medallion of Stefan Banach on the wall of a building
of the old JKU, in 1992.

JKU as seen on a 1938 postcard.

JKU as seen on a 1938 postcard.

LWÓW. Uniwersytet Jana Kazimierza. — L'Université.

JKU as seen on a 1939 postcard.

JKU – presently the Iwan Franko University –
from a contemporary photograph.

In this building the "Scottish Café" was located,
from a contemporary photograph.

"Roma Café" (on the left) and the "Scottish Café" (on the right)
on Fredro Place - from a 1916 postcard.

Inside of the "Scottish" Café - from a pre-war postcard.

Lvov Polytechnic - from a pre-war postcard c. 1910-1915.

Lvov Polytechnic - from a contemporary photograph.

there came into existence the so-called, and now famous, *Scottish Book* containing a collection of mathematics problems that the Lvov mathematicians challenged each other with (and also at the same time other world mathematicians), and which included the solutions to some of the problems.

The list of Scottish Café guests who entered problems in the *Scottish Book* was as follows. Stefan Banach was an author or co-author of 25 problems. The others were:

Stanisław Ulam (62 problems),
Stanisław Mazur (49),
Władysław Orlicz (14),
Józef Schreier (10),
Hugo Steinhaus (10),
Herman Auerbach (8),
Juliusz Schauder (7),
Samuel Eilenberg (6),
Max Eidelheit (5)
Stanisław Ruziewicz (5),
Mark Kac (4),
Władysław Nikliborc (4),
Edward Szpilrajn (Edward Marczewski) (4),
Maurice Fréchet (2),
Bronisław Knaster (2),
Kazimierz Kuratowski (2),
Stanisław Saks (2),
Ludwig Sternbach(2),
A.J. Ward (2),
Pavel Alexandrov (1),
Nikolai N. Bogolyubov (1),
Karol Borsuk (1),
Kampé de Fériet (1),
A.F. Fermant (1),
Leopold Infeld (1),
Stefan Kaczmarz (1),
Lazar Lusternik (1),
Antoni Łomnicki (1),
Józef Marcinkiewicz (1),
John von Neumann (1),
A. Cyril Offord (1),

Wacław Sierpiński (1),
Sergei Sobolev (1),
Simion Stoilov (1),
Rolin Wavre (1),
Antoni Zygmund (1).

Anyone who entered a problem would offer a prize to the person who came up with the solution. Different sorts of prizes were offered: a bottle of wine (funded by Banach, Mazur, Ulam, Sobolev)), a bottle of whisky ("of non-zero measure") (von Neumann) , a bottle of brandy (Bogolyubov), a bottle of champagne (Lusternik), a few small beers (Mazur, Knaster),), a small coffee (Steinhaus), 100 grams of caviar (Steinhaus), 1 kilogram of bacon (Saks), a lunch in the *Dorothy* restaurant in Cambridge (Ward) , a dinner in the best hotel in Lvov: the *George* (Steinhaus), , a "fondue" in Geneva and "fondant" in Lvov (Wavre) , and even a live goose (Mazur) .

The *Scottish Book* went through some tempestuous times during the years after it came into existence. The Soviets arrived in the city shortly after the outbreak of war and the later entries in the book clearly indicate that it was Soviet mathematicians who had made them. Following established "protocol" they too promised prizes for solutions to the problems they entered in it.

Łucja Banach took the *Scottish Book* with her to Wrocław after World War II. After her death in 1954 it passed into the hands of son Stefan Banach Jr, a neurosurgeon, and subsequent to his death into the possession of his close family (his widow and two daughters) where it now resides.

Roman Kałuża wrote [19]:

> For Polish mathematicians the Scottish Book *became an almost holy relic. Copies of it have been circulated worldwide but the original is exhibited only rarely. At the urging of Steinhaus a new notebook was purchased in Wrocław and was named the* New Scottish Book [11]. *It was in use between 1946 and 1948 and fulfilled a role similar to that of the original* Scottish Book *in Lvov. It was in the care of Professors Marczewski*[12] *and Steinhaus. The tradition of the* Scottish Book *was thus continued. However, the new version lacked the mythical and legendary qualities that have characterized the original, the unique and inimitable only one.*

At Steinhaus' direction the *Scottish Book* was transcribed in type. In 1957, Ulam had the book translated into English and distributed copies of the translation among mathematicians [38].

---

[11]See Ref. [67].
[12]Edward Marczewski (Edward Szpilrajn) (1907–1977).

1.5   The Dark Years

At the time the Soviet army first occupied Lvov on 22 September 1939, the schools were all open and instruction was in the Polish language. Banach was still a professor at Lvov University and was also dean of the Mathematics and Philosophy Faculty there. He was shortly later elected a Corresponding Member of the Ukrainian Soviet Republic's Academy of Sciences. Although always reluctant to get involved in politics he accepted the nomination to be a delegate member of the Lvov City Council. He also kept well informed about and eagerly followed the work and significant achievements of his former coworkers and students in the USA.

Years later Stefan Banach Jr recalled:

> *My father was invited to a conference in Kiev, two days before the war broke out between Germany and the Soviet Union. He went there and when he came back the war had started. He had immediately taken the last train to Lvov and arrived just before the Germans took over the city. I dared to ask him in private why he did not stay (in Kiev). He looked at me for a while and then he shrugged and told me that he loved us and that was the way every Banach behaved.*

German troops entered Lvov during the night of 30 June/1 July 1941, three days after the Soviets had fled the city. Its inhabitants were still under the shock of the monstrous crime perpetrated by the NKGB[13] on several thousand prisoners. On 2 July, the Germans arrested Professor Kazimierz Bartel[14] at the Polytechnic. During the night of 3/4 July, SS and Gestapo formations arrested a group of 22 professors of the Jan Kazimierz University, the Lvov Polytechnic and the Veterinary Academy. They shot them all on the Wulka Hills near Lvov at dawn on 4 July [45].

During the time between 1939 and 1945 the Polish School of Mathematics suffered very heavy losses. Many mathematicians were murdered. Among them were:

Herman Auerbach (1901–1942),
Kazimierz Bartel (1882–1941),
Max Eidelheit (1910–1943),
Antoni Hoborski (1879–1940),
Stefan Kaczmarz (1895–1940),
Stefan Jan Kempisty (1892–1940),
Michał Kerner (1902–1943),

---

[13]NKGB (People's Commissariat for State Security) – the Soviet secret police, intelligence and counter-intelligence service.

[14]See biographical note B-4.

Mojżesz D. Kirszbraun (1903 or 1904–1942),
Stanisław Marian Kołodziejczyk (1907–1939),
Adolf Lindenbaum (1901–1942),
Antoni Łomnicki (1881–1941),
Józef Marcinkiewicz (1910–1940),
Aleksander Rajchman (1890 –1940),
Stanisław Ruziewicz (1889–1941),
Stanisław Saks (1897–1942),
Juliusz Paweł Schauder (1899–1943),
Józef Schreier (1908–1942),
Włodzimierz Stożek (1883–1941)
Zygmunt Zalcwasser (1898–1943).

Some died from natural causes and war privations:

Leon Chwistek (1884–1944),
Samuel Dickstein (1851–1939),
Stefan Mazurkiewicz (1888–1945),
Witold Wilkosz (1891–1941)
Stanisław Zaremba (1863–1942), and many others.

During the German occupation of Lvov (1941 to 1944) Banach, together with numerous other academicians, various cultural figures, some members of the resistance, as well as school and university students, including his own son (a medical student), was able to secure employment only at the Institute for Typhus Studies[15]. It operated under the direction of Professor Rudolf Weigl[16] and included experiments that required the feeding of lice with human blood. It was a study of importance and urgent interest to the German military and, therefore, provided the participants with an invaluable document that afforded them protection from persecution by the occupiers.

At the outbreak of World War II the Biology Faculty at the Jan Kazimierz University in Lvov, working in response to the needs of the Polish Government's Ministry of the Army, was producing large quantities of a vaccine against epidemic typhus. It was for this reason that, following the Soviet occupation of Lvov, on 22 November 1939, the Weigl Institute was incorporated into the newly created Institute of Bacteriology and Sanitary Science, and the Professor was ordered to continue with the production of

---

[15] See the recollections of Professor Szybalski in chapter 3.6.
[16] See biographical note B-23.

the vaccine. Thereafter, with the exception of small quantities for civilian use, the rest was being shipped to the Soviet Union to protect the Red Army. In June 1941, the armed forces of the Third Reich attacked the Soviet Union and entered Lvov. The Institute, then called the Institute of Epidemiology and Sanitary Science, was renamed *Institut für Fleckfieber und Virusforschung des OKH.* and, together with the Weigl Institute, came under the control of the Germans. Profesor Weigl was left in charge as Director of the Institute and required to continue, and even to increase, the production of the vaccine. A building on Potocki Street, at one time part of the Queen Jadwiga Grammar School, and more recently used by the Soviets, was provided for this end, and the entire production of the vaccine was earmarked for use by the German land armies.

As mentioned by Professor Stefan Kryński [63]:

> It was the highly complicated situation the academic staff found itself in July 1941, that motivated Weigl to continue to run the Institute. He saw, thereby, an opportunity to help the large group of professors and their assistants who had been left deprived of work and position. He successfully extorted the Germans to allow him to take full responsibility for and decide alone whom to choose to be on his staff. The Institute thus grew quickly in size. An unusual and unique group was formed to produce the vaccine for epidemic typhus. It consisted of not just the academics but also of the youth conspiring against the occupiers and threatened with deportation to Germany, and fighters in the underground resistance. Their only common link with the Institute was the work permit they each received.

Banach's work at the Institute lasted until the end of the Nazi occupation of Lvov, that is, until July 1944. He was shortly thereafter offered the Chair of Mathematics at the Jagiellonian University in Krakow, but his serious illness, and ultimate death, prevented him from assuming the position.

Many years later Stefan Banach Jr related:

> During that time my father came and visited me in Krakow in 1944. He spent a couple of days there and looked better (...). He told me that he was "switching" to study physics problems and had some ideas that should win him the Nobel Prize. Our parting was sad and tinged with a sense of hopelessness. Reality dealt us a blow worse than we could have imagined because that was the last time I saw him.

Władysław Nikliborc (1889–1948) took selfless and very attentive care of the gravely ill Banach during the last few months of his life.

Stefan Banach Jr recalled:

> For several months Nikliborc nursed my father and my grieving mother and was

a guardian and messenger boy for them. I do not know how within this little person there could be so much heart and courage.

Stefan Banach died from lung cancer on 31 August 1945. He died in Lvov, at the house where he had been staying with his friends, the Riedl family, and was interred in their family sepulcher in the Łyczaków Cemetery in Lvov, next to the tomb of Maria Konopnicka[17].

Stefan Banach died before his time at the young age of 53 when still full of plans and ideas, and with a very promising future ahead of him.

1.6 Epilogue

Functional analysis which Banach created continued to spread to countless mathematics centers throughout the world. His ideas and discoveries have been bearing fruit and radiating to all the continents. The designation *Polish School of Mathematics*, of which he was the pillar, architect and founder, has become a symbol of excellence.

The name of Stefan Banach has already been cited 12,000 times in mathematics publications worldwide. As of December 2006, the Google Internet search engine has indexed more than one million pages in which the term *Banach space* appears (in various languages). The term *Banach algebras* appears approximately 200,000 times, and the *Hahn-Banach theorem* 100,000 times.

In 1946, the Polish Mathematical Society established the Stefan Banach Award, and the Polish Academy of Sciences has conferred a special Stefan Banach medal since 1992. Many schools and streets have been, and continue to be, named after him, and in 1972 the International Stefan Banach Mathematical Center was established. In 1999 in Krakow, a statue of Stefan Banach was unveiled on the 54th anniversary of his death.

Mark Kac (1914–1984), who considered Banach "probably the greatest Polish mathematician of all times" [14], wrote [18]:

Banach was the unquestioned superstar of Polish mathematics and his name is known wherever mathematics is taught. In the short fifty-three years of his life (...) he succeeded in combining an overwhelming flow of brilliant ideas with a style of high living that few men could sustain.

---

[17]Maria Konopnicka (1842–1910) – renowned Polish poet, a novelist, author of children's books.

Steinhaus finished his address at the Stefan Banach memorial conference with the words [80]:

Banach gave to Polish science, and particularly to Polish mathematics, more than anyone else. (...) He combined within himself a spark of genius with an astonishing internal urge, which addressed him incessantly in the words of the poet: "there is only one thing: the ardent glory of one's craft" [18] *– and mathematicians well know that their craft consists of the same secret as the poets' craft.*

(Translated by *Anna Markiewicz*
with comments of *John Greczek*)

1.7 Timetable to Stefan Banach's Life

1892 Stefan Banach is born on 30 March 1892, as the illegitimate child of Katarzyna Banach (1864–?) and Stefan Greczek (1868–1967). He does not know his mother who, after he is born and christened, gives him up to be raised by the family of Franciszka Płowa.

1902 At age 10, after completing education at a public primary school, he is enrolled at the Henryk Sienkiewicz Grammar School IV in Krakow.

1910 He graduates from grammar school and studies for a short time at the Jagiellonian University. He works for a living as a private tutor and as a bookshop assistant.

1911 He departs for Lvov and begins studies at the Lvov Polytechnic. He continues there until 1913 and earns a diploma.

1914 World War I breaks out and Stefan Banach returns to Krakow.

1915 He meets Hugo Steinhaus in the Planty Gardens in Krakow.

1917 He leaves for Lvov to attend Steinhaus' postdoctoral dissertation in mathematics.

1918 World War I ends and Poland regains its independence. The defence of Lvov during the Polish-Ukrainian War of 1918–1919.

1919 He becomes a founding member of the Polish Mathematical Society in Krakow.

1919 A first joint paper with Steinhaus appears in a Bulletin of the Krakow Academy: "Sur la convergence en moyenne de séries de Fourier" (On the Mean Convergence of Fourier Series).

1920 He leaves for Lvov and works as an assistant to Professor Antoni Łomnicki at the Lvov Polytechnic, continuing until 1922.

---

[18]"Il n'y a que la gloire ardente du métier (Verlaine).

1920 At Lvov University he presents his thesis titled "Sur les opérations dans les ensembles abstracts et leur application aux équations intégrales" (On Operators Defined on Abstract Sets and Their Applications to Integral Equations). Despite not having completed a full course of undergraduate studies, Banach is awarded a doctorate for this work, after the University waives the prerequisite academic requirements for that degree. He had previously already published 6 papers, however, this is the first one dedicated to linear operation theory.

1920 He and Łucja Braus (1897–1954) are married.

1922 He presents his post-doctoral thesis to be qualified as Assistant Professor at the Jan Kazimierz University.

1922 His and Łucja's son is born, Stefan Jr (d. 1999).

1922 He is appointed to the position of head of the Mathematics and Natural Sciences Faculty of the Jan Kazimierz University. He holds this position until 1939.

1923 He is chosen Vice-President of the Polish Mathematical Society, a position he holds until 1936.

1924 He becomes a corresponding member of the Polish Academy of Arts and Sciences.

1924 He publishes the paper "Sur la décomposition des ensembles de parties respectivement congruentes" (On Dissection of Sets of Points into Equal Parts), jointly with Alfred Tarski.

1924 He spends a year in France on a scholarship awarded by the Polish Government.

1927 He is appointed Full Professor at the Jan Kazimierz University.

1929 He writes textbooks of advanced and grammar-school level mathematics. Volumes I and II of *Differential and Integral Calculus* [2] are published in 1929 and 1930, respectively. Others, authored either solely by him, or jointly with Włodzimierz Stożek or Wacław Sierpiński, are published between then and 1938.

1929 Jointly with Steinhaus he is the founder and editor of the periodical *Studia Mathematica*.

1929 He writes the renowned monograph *Theory of Operations*, Vol. 1 *Theory of Linear Operations* [3], which he dedicates to his wife Łucja. Published in 1931, and translated into French the following year, it becomes the first treatise in the world on the subject of the general treatment of linear and metric spaces. This is one of the most important contributions to mathematics in the 20th century.

1931 He is elected President of the Mathematics and Physics Society of the students of Jan Kazimierz University. He holds this office until 1933 and takes an active part in the Society's activities that include excursions in and around Lvov. He remains an active member until 1939.

1935 The first problem entered by Banach in the *Scottish Book* is dated 17 July 1935, and the last, entered by Steinhaus, is dated 31 May 1941.

1936 He is invited to attend the International Mathematics Congress in Oslo, where he delivers the plenary lecture on "Die Theorie der Operationen und ihre Bedeutung für die Analysis" (Theory of Operators and Their Significance in Analysis).

1939 He is awarded a prize by the Polish Academy of Arts and Sciences.

1939 He is elected President of the Polish Mathematical Society, a position he holds until 1945.

1939 Soviet troops enter Lvov on 22 September. Banach is appointed professor of the Ukrainian National Ivan Franko University (1940–1941, 1944–1945), converted from the former Jan Kazimierz University. He holds the chair of Mathematical Analysis.

1939 He is appointed Dean of the Mathematics and Natural Science Faculty of the Ivan Franko University, a position he holds until 1941.

1939 He is appointed a corresponding member of the Ukrainian Science Academy of the Soviet Socialist Republics. He is invited, together with his associates, to attend conferences and symposia in Moscow and Leningrad, and to lecture there.

1940 He is invited by the Organizing Committee of the New York World Congress of Mathematicians to be section chairman at the congress.

1940 He is elected a member of the Lvov City Council.

1941 In June 1941, Nazi troops enter Lvov. In autumn he begins working as a feeder of lice in the Institute for Epidemic Typhus and Virus Research (Institut für Fleckfieber-und Virusforschung d. OKH Dienststelle Lemberg) headed by Professor Rudolf Weigl. (Stefan Jr, his son, a student of medicine, also works there). Banach works at the Institute until it is evacuated to the West in March 1944.

1944 Soviet troops enter Lvov on 27 July 1944. Banach is once again Professor of Mathematics and the Dean of the Mathematics and Natural Sciences Faculty. He resides, together with his family, in a villa belonging to the Riedl family (on Dwernicki Street). Already afflicted with an incurable illness, he nevertheless begins to organize his research and teaching responsibilities at the National Lvov University.

He assumes a leadership position in the Lvov Mathematics Society. He is a member of the editing staff of the journal *Matematicheskii Sbornik*. He becomes involved with the currents of political life and is active in the Pan-Slavic Antifascism Committee.

1945 He becomes a board member of Pan-Slavic Antifascism Committee in Sofia.

1945 He dies of lung cancer in Lvov on 31 August 1945. He is interred in the Riedl family sepulcher at the Łyczaków Cemetery in Lvov.

(Translated by *John Greczek*)

KARTKA POCZTOWA

1892·1945

STEFAN BANACH

40·POLSKA·6R

JUBILEUSZOWY ZJAZD
POLSKIEGO TOWARZYSTWA
MATEMATYCZNEGO

KRAKÓW
1 9 6 9

P.P T.,1 VII 69 200 000 proj. H. Chylinski

The facsimile of a postcard issued on the occasion of a jubilee meeting of the
Polish Mathematical Society, in 1969, in Krakow, to commemorate its fiftieth
anniversary. The choice of the image on it of Stefan Banach is emphatic witness
to the recognition of his greatness.

PAMIĘCI
ZAMORDOWANYCH UCZONYCH

Niemcy zamordowali miljony ludzi. Nie można o wszystkich napisać, lecz ból zmusza mnie do wspomnienia o dwóch bliskich mi polskich uczonych, którzy zginęli z rąk hitlerowskich katów.

W pierwszych dniach po wkroczeniu Niemców do Lwowa zostało zabranych z domu przeszło 20 profesorów wyższych uczelni, najwybitniejszych przedstawicieli nauki i sztuki. Zawleczono ich na wzgórza wuleckie i tam rozstrzelano. Dlaczego ich zabrano, nikt nie wie. Winą ich było to, że rozwijali kulturę polską, że godnie ją reprezentowali. Ponieśli śmierć męczeńską. Krew ich nie została przelana bezkarnie. Z krwi tej wyrosną mściciele. Chwała Czerwonej Armji, która pierwsza zadała miażdżące ciosy „niezwyciężonej" armji Hitlera i pokazała Niemcom, że za zbrodnie czeka ich odwet.

Pamiętnej nocy lipcowej 1941 roku siepacze Hitlera przyszli po Włodzimierza Stożka, profesora matematyki na Politechnice Lwowskiej. Była godzina 11 w nocy. Wyciągnęli go z łóżka, kazali mu się ubrać i iść z nimi. Zobaczyli jego synów. Jeden, ukończony inżynier, drugi student 4 roku chemji, niezwykle zdolny, w przyszłości napewno wybitny uczony. Trzeci, 16-letni chłopiec, uczeń szkoły średniej. Dwóch starszych zabrali z ojcem, trzeci wydał im się za młody. Gestapowcy mieli rozkaz aresztować ojca, synów zabrali z wielkiej gorliwości, bez rozkazu.

Prof. Włodzimierz Stożek, wybitny matematyk, był autorem wielu prac z teorji równań całkowych, z teorji potencjału i wielu innych dziedzin matematyki. Prace jego są szeroko znane również zagranicą. Była to piękna postać, wybitny naukowiec i znakomity pedagog, kochany przez młodzież jako człowiek o gołębiem sercu. Pomagał ze wszystkich sił każdemu, kto się do niego zwracał o pomoc. Nie znał różnic narodowościowych. My, którzyśmy z nim blisko żyli, dziś bardziej oceniamy jego postać świetlaną i jego wielkie zasługi dla kultury. Zostanie w naszej pamięci jako wielki uczony, jako człowiek, który kochał ludzkość i wiernie jej służył.

Tej strasznej nocy przyszli mordercy hitlerowscy po profesora Antoniego Łomnickiego. Lwowianin, przez dwadzieścia kilka lat pracował na Politechnice Lwowskiej jako profesor matematyki. Setki inżynierów przygotował do zawodu. Byłem jego asystentem. On pierwszy wskazał mi, jak wielkie i odpowiedzialne jest zadanie profesora. Był to wybitny pedagog, jeden z największych, jakich znałem, autor wielu popularnych podręczników dla szkół średnich, autor jednego z najlepszych, przewyższającego zagraniczne, podręczników analizy wyższej dla techników. Na wysokim poziomie stoi jego dzieło, traktujące o kartografji. Równie wielka, jak pedagogiczna, była działalność naukowa profesora Łomnickiego. Najważniejsza praca jego, znana i cytowana w świecie naukowym, podaje związek między rachunkiem prawdopodobieństwa a miarą Lebeguca. Profesor Łomnicki był człowiekiem ogromnej energji i pracy. Wielu jego byłych asystentów, będących dzisiaj profesorami wyższych zakładów naukowych, zawdzięcza mu przygotowanie do zawodu pedagogicznego. Prof. Łomnicki był powszechnie lubiany i poważany; miał wielu przyjaciół, którzy wysoko cenili jego zalety duchowe. Niemcy zamordowali prof. Łomnickiego, bo—chociaż był uczonym — w ich tępych, skarłowaciałych umysłach był tak samo niebezpieczny, jak żołnierz uzbrojony w karabin.

Prof. dr STEFAN BANACH,

prezes Polskiego Towarzystwa Matematycznego, redaktor czasopisma „Studia Mathematica", laureat Polskiej Akademji Nauk w roku 1939.

The facsimile of an article by Stefan Banach "*In Remembrance of the Murdered Scholars*" (Pamięci zamordowanych uczonych) about Włodzimierz Stożek and Antoni Łomnicki . Moscow, the weekly Organ of the Polish Patriot Association nr 46, 18 December 1944. (Translated by *John Greczek*)

IN REMEMBRANCE
OF THE MURDERED SCHOLARS

The Germans murdered millions of people. It is not possible to write about them all but the pain I feel forces me to write in memory of two Polish scholars who were close to me and who perished at the hands of Hitler's executioners.

During the first few days after the Germans entered Lvov they took from their homes over 20 professors who taught at the higher educational institutions and who were the most prominent in their fields of science and art. They dragged them off to the Wuleckie Hills and shot them. Why they were taken nobody knows. Their guilt was that they were promoting Polish culture and represented it with dignity. They died like martyrs. Their blood was not spilled with impunity. It will be avenged. Glory be to the Red Army which was the first to inflict crushing blows on Hitler's "invincible" army and showed the Germans that retribution awaits their crimes.

On a memorable night in July 1941 Hitler's slayers came for Włodzimierz Stożek, a professor of mathematics at the Lvov Polytechnic. It was 11 o'clock at night. They pulled him out of bed and ordered him to get dressed and come with them. They saw his sons. One was a graduate engineer, another was a very talented fourth year chemistry student, no doubt with promise in the future to become an outstanding scholar. The third was a 16 year old boy, a high school student. The two older boys they took with their father, the third one seemed to them to be too young. The Nazi killers had orders only to arrest the father but in their great zeal took the sons too.

Professor Włodzimierz Stożek was an outstanding mathematician, the author of numerous papers on the theory of integral equations, potential theory, as well as on many other branches of mathematics. His work is widely known in Poland and also abroad. He had a very charming personality and was a distinguished scholar, beloved by his young students as someone with a very caring heart. He was always ready to assist anyone who asked for his help. He took little notice of nationality differences. Those of us who were close to him and knew him well now esteem even more highly his enlightened personality and great cultural contributions. He will be remembered as a great intellectual who loved all of humanity and served it faithfully.

That dreadful night Hitler's assassins also came for Professor Antoni Łomnicki. A native of Lvov, he worked for over twenty years as a mathematics professor at the Lvov Polytechnic. He prepared hundreds of engineers for their profession. I was his assistant. He was the first to instill in me the importance and responsibility of a professor's task. He was an unrivaled educator, one of the best I ever knew. He was the author of many popular schoolbooks as well as textbooks on advanced analysis for technologists, surpassing in quality those published abroad. His work in the field of cartography was at a high level. Equally effective were his teaching and pedagogic efforts. Professor Łomnicki had tremendous energy and a great work ethic. Many of his assistants, who are now professors at institutions of higher learning, are grateful to him for the way he prepared them for careers in education. Professor Łomnicki was universally well liked and respected; he had many friends who highly valued his spiritual qualities. The Germans slaughtered Professor Łomnicki because – even although he was a scholar – in their warped and dwarfish minds he was as dangerous as a soldier with a rifle.

Professor Dr. STEFAN BANACH

President Polish Mathematical Society, Editor of the Journal "Studia Mathematica", 1939 Laureate of the Polish Academy of Science.

Translation of an article by Stefan Banach "*In Remembrance of the Murdered Scholars*" (Pamięci zamordowanych uczonych) about Włodzimierz Stożek and Antoni Łomnicki . Moscow, the weekly Organ of the Polish Patriot Association nr 46, 18 December 1944. (Translated by *John Greczek*)

1.8   The Laureates of the Stefan Banach Awards

Starting in 1992, the Polish Academy of Sciences has awarded *the Stefan Banach medal* to individuals in recognition of their outstanding contributions to the advancement of mathematics. The past medalists are as follows[19]:

1992 Zbigniew Ciesielski (Poland)
1992 Stanisław Łojasiewicz (Poland)
1992 Czesław Olech (Poland)
1992 Czesław Ryll-Nardzewski (Poland)
1992 Andrzej Schinzel (Poland)
1996 Aleksander Pełczyński (Poland)
1997 Joram Lindenstrauss (Israel)
1998 Kazimierz Urbanik (Poland)
1999 Friedrich Hirzebruch (Germany)
2000 Wiesław Żelazko (Poland)
2001 Gilles Pisier (France)
2004 Tadeusz Figiel (Poland)
2004 Nigel J. Kalton (USA)
2007 William B. Johnson (USA)

The Stefan Banach prize has been awarded, since 1946, by the Polish Mathematical Society for work that "by means of significant new results advances scientific knowledge". The list of prize winners is as follows [20]:

Hugo Steinhaus (1946),
Mieczysław Biernacki (1947),
Władysław Orlicz (1948),
Stanisław Mazur (1949),
Jan Mikusiński (1950),
Adam Bielecki (1951),
Andrzej Alexiewicz (1952),
Stanisław Hartman (1953),
Tadeusz Leżański (1954),
Witold Wolibner (1955),
Zofia Szmydt (1956),

---

[19]See http://www.impan.gov.pl/EN/ – the official website of the Institute of Mathematics of the Polish Academy of Sciences.

[20]The list is based on the information from a website of the Polish Mathematical Society (http://www.impan.gov.pl/ptm/).

Andrzej Grzegorczyk (1957),
Mieczysław Altman (1958),
Józef Meder (1959),
Krzysztof Maurin (1960),
Czesław Bessaga and Aleksander Pełczyński (1961),
Edward Sąsiada (1962),
Bogdan Bojarski (1963),
Zbigniew Ciesielski (1964),
Jan Mycielski (1965),
Włodzimierz Mlak (1966),
Wiesław Żelazko (1967),
Władysław Narkiewicz (1968),
Danuta Przeworska-Rolewicz and Stefan Rolewicz (1969),
Roman Duda (1970),
Stanisław Kwapień (1971),
Andrzej Pelczar (1972),
Adam Henryk Toruńczyk (1973),
Leszek Pacholski (1974),
Tadeusz Figiel (1976),
Lech Drewnowski (1977),
Przemysław Wojtaszczyk (1979),
Lech Maligranda (1982),
Tadeusz Byczkowski (1983),
Marek Bożejko (1984),
Wojciech Banaszczak (1985),
Henryk Hudzik (1986),
Jarosław Zemanek (1987),
Adam Paszkiewicz (1988),
Marek Lassak (1990),
Paweł Domański (1991),
Marek Nawrocki (1992),
Ryszard Szwarc (1993),
Mariusz Lemańczyk (1997),
Mieczysław Mastyło (2001),
Rafał Latała and Krzysztof Oleszkiewicz (2002),
Jerzy Jezierski and Wacław Marzantowicz (2003).

The 3-year-old Stefan Banach in the Planty Park in Krakow.

Stefan Banach at about 5 years of age.

Henryk Siemiradzki and
Stefan Banach playing
chess, c. 1898.

Stefan Banach with
Franciszka Plowa,
c. 1900.

Juliusz Mien (1842-1905).

Stefan Banach on the day of his
first Holy Communion.

Stefan Banach during his first
year in grammar school,
1902/1903.

Stefan Banach, aged 12,
with Jozef Siemiradzki.

Stefan Banach (on the left)
during his third year
of grammar school, 1904/1905.

Stefan Banach during his fourth
year in grammar school,
1905/1906.

Stefan Banach during his sixth
year in grammar school,
1907/1908.

Stefan Banach during his seventh
year in grammar school,
1908/1919.

Stefan Banach at 18 years of age,
after receiving his grammar
school diploma ("Matura"), 1910.

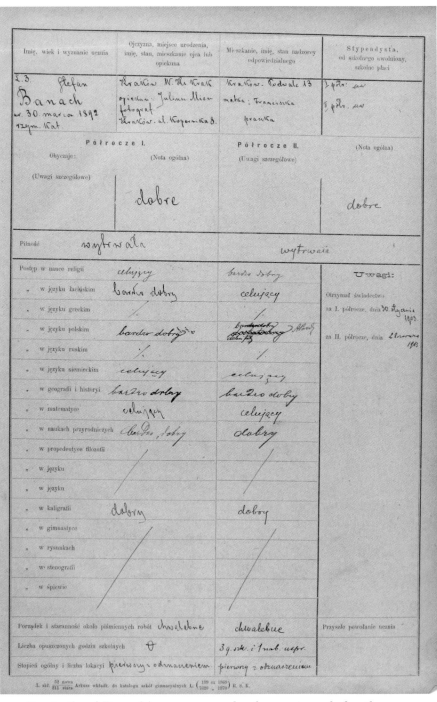

Facsimile of Banach's grammar school report card, for the year 1902-1903.

Name, age and rel.denomination of student.	Native country, birthplace, name, employment, address of father or guardian.	Address, name, employment of responsible caretaker.	Grant recipient, exempt from school fees, paying school fees.
L.3 **Stefan B a n a c h** Birthdate: 30 March 1892 Roman Catholic.	Krakow in the Great Duchy of Krakow. Guardian Juliusz Mien photographer Krakow Kopernika St. # 8	Krakow. Podwale 13 mother: Franciszka, laundress.	I semester exempt. II semester exempt.

Semester I		**Semester II**	(Overall accomplishment)
Manners (Specific comments)	(Overall accomplishment)	(Specific comments)	
	good		good
Dilligence	persistent	persistent	

	Semester I	Semester II	Remarks
Progress in religious education	excellent	very good	
" in Latin	very good	excellent	Received certificate
" in Greek	—	—	For semester I on 30 January, 1903
" in Polish	very good	very good	For semester II on 28 June, 1903
" in Russian	—	—	
" in German	excellent	excellent	
" in geography and history	very good	very good	
" in mathematics	excellent	excellent	
" in natural history	very good	good	
" in introduction to philosophy	—	—	
" in ....language	—	—	
" in..........language	—	—	
" in calligraphy	good	good	
" in gymnastics	—	—	
" in drawing	—	—	
" in stenography	—	—	
" in singing	—	—	
	—	—	
Neatness and accuracy of written work	exemplary	exemplary	Student's future vocation
Number of hours absent from school	0	3 school hrs and 1 absence excused	
Overall classification and ranking	first with distinction	first with distinction	

Banach's grammar school report card, for the year 1902-1903 (translation).

L. 1 U c z e ń	Opłata szkolna (płaci lub uwolniony reskryptem)	Rodzaj przyjęcia

Nazwisko: *Banach*	I. półr. *uwolniony*	
Imię: *Stefan*	II. półr. *nto*	2
Dzień i rok urodzenia: *30 marca 1892.*	Stypendyum (fundacya, kwota, reskrypt)	Wyciąg z świadectwa, przyniesionego z zakładu innego:
Miejsce urodzenia: *Kraków*		
Państwo (kraj koronny): *Wielkie Księstwo Krakowskie*		
Przynależność państwowa: *Austrya*		
Wyznanie: *rzym. kat.*		
Język ojczysty: *polski*		

Imię i nazwisko	ojca (matki)	opiekuna	odpowiedzialnego nadzorcy	gospodarza, u którego uczeń mieszka
	—	*Stefan Greczek*		*Franciszka Płowa*
Stan	—	*asst. przy urzędzie pocztw.*		*bez zajęcia*
Mieszkanie	—	*Zwierzyniec ul. Lelewela 15.*		*Garncarska 5.*

Świadectwo roczne	Wynik ogólny	Uwagi

Zachowanie się: *dobre*		
Postęp w przedmiotach nauki:		
W nauce religii: *bardzo dobry*		
W języku łacińskim: *dostateczny*		
W języku greckim: *dostateczny*		
W języku polskim: *Dobry*		
W języku ruskim: —	Do klasy następnej	
W języku niemieckim: *dostateczny.*		
W geografii i historyi: *dostateczny*	uzdolniony.	
W matematyce: *bardzo dobry z odzn.*		
W fizyce: *bardzo dobry z odznaczeniem*		
W propedeutyce filozofii: *dobry*		
Przedmioty nadobowiązkowe:		
w drugiem ojus. *dostateczny*		
	Otrzymał świadectwo roczne	
Liczba opuszczonych godzin szkolnych: *31/lvl.* z nich nie usprawiedliwiono *4*	z dnia *29 czerw. 1909.*	

L. składu 52. Katalog główny dla gimnazyów. Arkusz wkładowy.

Facsimile of Banach's grammar school report card, for the year 1908-1909.

L. 1 Student	School Fees (payable or exempt)		Basis for admission
Surname: **Banach**	Semester I.	Exempt	2
First Name: **Stefan**	Semester II.	Exempt	
Birthdate: 30 March, 1892.	**Scholarship**		Extract from certificate presented from another institution
Birthplace: Kraków	Yes		
Country (crown territory) Grand Duchy of Krakow			
Country Affiliation: Austria Rel. Denomination: R. Catholic Native Language: Polish			

Name and Surname	father (mother)	Guardian	Responsible caretaker	Student's landlord
	—	Stefan Greczek	—	Franciszka Płowa
Employment	—	Assistant at the tax office	—	Without employment
Home address	—	Zwierzyniec ul. Lelewela 15	—	Garncarska 5

Year-end progress report		General result	Comments
General Behavior	good		
Progress in academic subjects			
Religion:	very good		
Latin:	satisfactory		
Greek:	satisfactory		
Polish:	good		
Russian:	—		
German:	satisfactory	Qualified to advance to next higher class	
Geography and history:	satisfactory		
Mathematics:	very good with distinction		
Physics:	very good with distinction		
Introduction to philosophy:	good		
Elective subjects:			
History of fatherland.	satisfactory		
Number of hours absent from school	31 including 4 unexcused.	Received year-end certificate dated 29 June, 1909.	

Banach's grammar school report card, for the year 1908-1909 (translation).

Stefan Banach at about 19 years of age.

Stefan Banach at about 22 years of age.

Stefan Banach at 27 years
of age. Krakow, 1919.

Łucja Braus at 18 years
of age in 1916.

Łucja Banach (nee Braus)
at about 25 years of age.

Łucja Banach at about 35
years of age.

Stefan Banach with his son
Stefan Jr. in 1923.

Stefan Banach with his son
Stefan Jr., c. 1924.

Łucja Banach with her son
Stefan Jr., Marseilles (France),
1925.

Stefan Banach with his son
Stefan Jr., Marseilles
(France), 1925.

From the left: Łucja Banach, Stefan Banach
with son Stefan Jr., c. 1927.

Stefan Banach with his son Stefan Jr., Lvov, 1930.

A meeting of the Mathematical and Physics Society, Lvov, 1930.
Sitting in the middle is Stefan Banach, sitting third from the left
is Leon Chwistek. Sitting first and third from the right, respectively,
are Stefan Kaczmarz and Stanisław Loria.

Mathematicians in a hall of the Jan Kazimierz University, Lvov, May,
1930. Standing (from the left): Kazimierz Kuratowski, Bronisław
Knaster, Stefan Banach, Włodzimierz Stożek, Eustachy Żyliński,
Stanisław Ruziewicz. Sitting: Hugo Steinhaus, Ernst Zermelo, Stefan
Mazurkiewicz.

Łucja Banach with son
Stefan Jr., Skole, 1933.

Stefan Banach with son Stefan Jr. during an outing of the
Mathematical and Physics Society, Lvov, 1931.

Stefan Banach with his wife
Łucja, Morszyn, 1935.

Stefan Banach with his wife
Łucja, Morszyn, 1935.

Stefan Banach at 43 years
of age, 1935.

Group of Polish mathematicians: Stefan Banach, Bronisław Knaster,
Kazimierz Zarankiewicz and Kazimierz Kuratowski, Oslo, 1936.

Stefan Banach at 44 years
of age, 1936.

Stefan Banach.

Stefan Banach Jr.
as a student of medicine, 1942.

Last photograph of Stefan Banach, c. 1943.

Riedl family sepulcher in which Stefan Banach was interred in the
Lyczakow Cemetery, Lvov.

Riedl family sepulcher in
which Stefan Banach
was interred in the
Lyczakow Cemetery,
Lvov.

Statue of Stefan Banach in front of the Mathematics and Physics
Institute of the Jagellonian University in Krakow.

Bust of Stefan Banach
in the Stefan Banach
International
Mathematical Center
in Warsaw.

Medallion with bust of Stefan Banach on the wall of a
building of the old Jan Kazimierz University, Lvov.

Medal of the Polish Academy of Science to
commemorate the hundredth anniversary of the birth
of Stefan Banach.

Postage stamp with image of Stefan Banach.

Chapter 2

Letters

2.1 First letter[1] from Stefan Banach to Stanisław Ulam[2]

Lvov, 10 December 1937[3].

Dear Sir,

I received your letter and I thank you for the news it contained. The mathematics questions you raised are interesting and I set about to try to resolve them but so far without success. I have been busy up to now with the mechanics (monograph) which I have finally completed[4]. There is nothing interesting happening here, except that lectures have been suspended due to arguments. I don't know if you know that Auerbach[5] was seriously ill (stomach ulcer) and spent a month in hospital. Now he is walking and feels better. There was nothing especially interesting at the mathematics meeting in Warsaw. Saks[6] has resigned (after waiting a long time) his chair at the University of Warsaw. Despite the fact that the mathematics commission did not want to accept his resignation the department voted to accept it and to advertise the opening. Supposedly Borsuk[7]

---

[1] Copy of the letter belonging to the archival collections of the Institute of Mathematics of the Polish Academy of Sciences, reproduced here with the kind permission of Professor Zbigniew Ciesielski.

[2] See biographical note B-20.

[3] On the letterhead: The Jan Kazimierz University in Lvov, 4 St. Nicholas Street, Institute of Mathematics.

[4] Banach refers to Ref. [4].

[5] Herman Auerbach (1901–1942).

[6] Stanisław Saks (1897–1942).

[7] Karol Borsuk (1905–1982).

is the favoured candidate but he is thought to have stated that in these circumstances he will not accept the chair. I am not sure about the underlined information as I have not verified it. Steinhaus relayed it to me, so let him be finally responsible for the eventual confirmation of its accuracy.

I am presently working on the measure in the spaces $(\mathcal{L}^2)$ and $(\mathcal{C})$. The problem I am concerned with can be given the following physical meaning: Given a mechanical system with infinitely many degrees of freedom. Given the probability p that the mechanical system falls into an area $\mathcal{G} \in E$ within the time interval between t' and t where E represents the space of possible positions of the system. Obviously $p = F(\mathcal{G}, t', t)$. The problem consists in determining what properties can be expected of the function F, that is, which of them can be specifically obtained, and next – what can be anticipated about the motion of the system, i.e., its velocity, acceleration, and so on, if we know the function F or its properties. This reduces to the investigation of a measure in the space $(\mathcal{C})$. Here is another example: A point A moves along the x-axis. Let $(t'_1, t_1), (t'_2, t_2), \ldots, (t'_n, t_n)$ represent nonoverlapping time intervals. Given is the probability p of the point A staying within the segment x'_1, x_1 in the time between t'_1 and t_1, within the segment x'_2, x_2 in the time between t'_2 and $t_2, \ldots$ within the segment x'_n, x_n in the time between t'_n and t_n. Obviously $p = F(x'_1, x_1, x'_2, x_2, \ldots, t'_1, t_1, \ldots, t'_n, t_n)$. Given the function F, what can be said about the motion, what properties of capital F can be assumed?

For the moment I only have some examples and the theorems are not deep yet. As I said before, this reduces to the investigation of the measure in the spaces $(\mathcal{C})$ and $(\mathcal{L}^2)$. I will let you know, if I have more interesting results. In any case I will try to present these questions to you in a more precise way, if you say that you consider them interesting. I am looking forward to your answer soon and perhaps to some information from you.

I would like at this time to correspond with you concerning my invitation to America, as I now am able to do so after finishing the mechanics (monograph). Please write a lot about mathematics, yours and that of others. I will refer it to the Mathematical Society.

Yours very sincerely,
S. Banach

P.S. I enclose for you the account of an interesting adventure that befell someone from Lvov.

(Translated by John Greczek and Wiktor Bartol)

Facsimile of the first letter of Stefan Banach to Stanisław Ulam (page 1).

(2)

gorii je nie zrozumieli tam. Opowiadał mi je Steinhaus, na którego niech spadnie obowiązek ewentualnego dowodu.

Zajmuję się obecnie miarą w przestrzeni $(L)^2$ i (C). Problemat, o którym chodzi mi, ma by nadać następujący sens fizykalny: Dany jest pewien układ mechaniczny o nieskończenie wielu stopniach swobody. Dane jest prawdopodobieństwo p na to, aby w czasie od t' do t'' położenie układu mechanicznego w pewien obszar $\mathcal{Q} \subset E$ gdzie E oznacza przestrzeń możliwych położeń układu. Oczywiście $p = F(\mathcal{Q}, t', t'')$. Chodzi o to aby ustalić, jakie własności można od funkcji F żądać, t.zn. jakie dadzą się konkretnie wyliczać, a następnie co można o ruchu układu, o jego prędkości, przyspieszeniu, itp. powiedzieć, jeżeli znamy F względnie jej własności. Sprowadza się to do badania miary w przestrzeni (C). Innym przykładem jest następujący: Punkt A porusza się po osi x. Niechaj (t'_1, t''_1), (t'_2, t''_2), .. (t'_n, t''_n) oznaczają przedziały czasu nie zachodzące na siebie. Dane jest prawdopodobieństwo na to aby punkt A znajdował się w czasie od t'_1 do t''_1 w odcinku x'_1, x''_1, w czasie od t'_2 do t''_2 w odcinku x'_2, x''_2 ... w czasie od t'_n do t''_n w odcinku x'_n, x''_n. Oczywiście $p = F(x'_1, x''_1, x'_2, x''_2, \ldots t'_1, t''_1, \ldots t'_n, t''_n)$. Znana jest funkcja F; co można o ruchu powiedzieć i jakie można własności o F zażądać.

ditto (page 2)

UNIWERSYTET
JANA KAZIMIERZA
WE LWOWIE, UL. ŚW. MIKOŁAJA L. 4

INSTYTUT MATEMATYCZNY

③

④

ditto (pages 3 & 4)

2.2   Second letter[8] from Stefan Banach
to Stanisław Ulam

Dear Stanisław,

I was very pleased to get your letter. There is really nothing interesting happening here. Borsuk was given the chair in Warsaw following Saks' resignation. In Lvov they are looking to appoint someone to the chair of the Department of Mechanical Engineering at the Polytechnic, but they don't want Nikliborc[9] (because he's not an engineer!). Auerbach is already feeling well. Szauder[10] has a daughter (she is now ± 3 weeks old). Poor Szauder complains that he can't sleep at night because his daughter is crying a lot. My mechanics (textbook) has not yet appeared, however, it is complete, and Knaster[11] swears that within two weeks it'll be on the shelves of the bookstores. Mazur[12] is doing a lot of work on linear-topological spaces. It appears that there is a Fixpunktsatz[13], in view of which Szauder is powerless and is no longer the record holder of the Fixpunktsatz. I am currently giving a seminar based on the most recent publications, just as in the previous years. Lvov has gained a young individual in the person of Mr Turowicz[14]. He is a young mathematician from Krakow. Maybe he will be able to accomplish something with us here. It seems from your letter that my visit to America is starting to become a reality. I'm very grateful to you for your involvement with the arrangements. Most important, of course, is the amount they are willing to pay, which should be adequate and suitable for a year's stay for me and my wife[15] and son[16].

---

[8]Copy of the letter belonging to the archival collections of the Institute of Mathematics of the Polish Academy of Sciences, reproduced here with the kind permission of Professor Zbigniew Ciesielski.

[9]Władysław Nikliborc (1889–1948).

[10]Juliusz Paweł Schauder (1896–1943).

[11]Bronisław Knaster (1893–1980).

[12]Stanisław Mazur (1905–1981).

[13]The Banach fixpoint theorem, also known as the contraction mapping theorem (or principle).

[14]Andrzej Turowicz (1904–1985).

[15]Łucja Banach (1897–1954) née Braus, wife of Stefan Banach.

[16]See biographical note B-3.

Facsimile of the second letter of Stefan Banach to Stanisław Ulam (page 1).

Z listu Pańskiego wynika, że przyjazd mój do Ameryki zaczyna być realny. Barodo Panu dziękuję, że Pan się w tym ragninje. Oczywiście najważniejsze jest rzeczą by kwota, którą chcę zapłacić i byda odpowiednio rozłamanej na rok pobytu mający z żoną i synem. W tym celu prosiłbym Pana o poinformowanie mnie w tej materii.[1] Prosiłbym Pana mówić o napisaniu mi, jakie co radzi mi pan na wyjechały do Ameryki przygotował. Zadgczam pewne uwagi z teorii miary w przestrzeni abstrak., cyjnych.

       Ściskam serdecznie dłoń

         S. Banach

Lwów dn. 14/II 1938
   Milowajów 4.

P.S. Chciałbym jeszcze wiedzieć kiedy mam się spodziewać honorariów (i.w. wszelkich) (miałem wrócić z Ameryki

1) T.w. Jakie są koszta utrzymania, whisky, wody itp.

In connection with that I would like to ask you to let me know about this matter (1). Please also write and let me know what you would advise me to prepare for my lectures in America. I enclose some comments pertaining to measure theory in abstract spaces.

Very sincerely yours,
S. Banach

Lvov, 14 February 1938
4 St. Nicholas Street.

P.S. I would also like to know when you expect to receive concrete (i.e. official) information from America. (1) i.e. what is the cost of living, whisky, soda, etc.

(Translated by *John Greczek*)

2.3 Stefan Banach's mathematical enclosure[17]

Let E be an arbitrary infinite set of functions $x(t)$ integrable in $(0 \leq t \leq 1)$ and satisfying the condition

$$\int_0^1 x(t)dt \leq 1 \tag{1}$$

[We do not assume that E is the set of all the functions satisfying (1)]. We consider E as a metric set with usual distance

$$(x_1, x_2) = \int_0^1 |x_1(t) - x_2(t)|dt \leq 1 \tag{2}$$

If δ_1, δ_2,... δ_n,... represent an arbitrary system (finite or not) of non-overlapping segments in the interval $(0, 1)$ and $(\alpha_1 \leq \beta_1)$, $(\alpha_2 \leq \beta_2)$, ... $(\alpha_n \leq \beta_n)$,... is an arbitrary system of pairs of real numbers, then the symbol

$$H(\delta_1, \delta_2, ...\delta_n; \alpha_1, \beta_1, \alpha_2, \beta_2, ...\alpha_n, \beta_n, ...)$$

denotes the set of those functions $x(t) \in E$ for which

$$\alpha_i \leq \int_{\delta_i} x(t)dt \leq \beta_i, \quad (i = 1, 2, ...n, ...) \tag{3}$$

---

[17]This is probably an attachment to the second letter. Copy of Banach's letter to Ulam from the collection of the American Mathematical Society in Philadelphia.

Assume that a Lebesgue (i.e. completely additive) measure is defined in E so that

A_1) The set E has measure 1.

A_2) Finite sets have measure zero.

A_3) Borel subsets of E are measurable.

Theorem 1.

There is no Lebesgue measure satisfying the conditions (A) and such that the relation

$$\text{measure}H(\delta_1, \delta_2, ...\delta_n; \alpha_1, \beta_1, \alpha_2, \beta_2, ...\alpha_n, \beta_n) \qquad (I)$$

$$= \text{measure}H(\delta_1, \alpha_1, \beta_1) \cdot \text{measure}H(\delta_2, \alpha_2, \beta_2) \cdots$$

$$\cdots \text{measure}H(\delta_n, \alpha_n, \beta_n)$$

is satisfied for every finite system of non-overlapping segments $\delta_1, \delta_2, ...\delta_n$ and arbitrary number pairs $(\alpha_1 \leq \beta_1)$, ... $(\alpha_n \leq \beta_n)$.

Theorem 2.

For every system (finite or not) of non-overlapping segments $\delta_1, \delta_2, ...\delta_n, ...$ there is a Lebesgue measure satisfying conditions (A) and such that the relation

$$\text{measure}H(\delta_1, \delta_2, ...\delta_n, ...; \alpha_1, \beta_1, \alpha_2, \beta_2, ...\alpha_n, \beta_n, ...)$$

$$= \text{measure}H(\delta_1, \alpha_1, \beta_1) \cdot \text{measure}H(\delta_2, \alpha_2, \beta_2) \cdots$$

$$\cdots \text{measure}H(\delta_n, \alpha_n, \beta_n) \cdots$$

is satisfied for every system of pairs of real numbers $(\alpha_1 \leq \beta_1)$, ... $(\alpha_n \leq \beta_n)$, ... **Note.** Theorem 1 can be expressed in stronger terms:

Theorem 1*).

For every Lebesgue measure satisfying conditions (A) one can find a number $\epsilon > 0$ such that if the segment $(0, 1)$ is partitioned into non-overlapping segments $\delta_1, \delta_2, ...\delta_n$ each of length less than ϵ, then (I) is not satisfied for every system of numbers $(\alpha_1 \leq \beta_1),... (\alpha_n \leq \beta_n)$.

The above theorems imply an interesting corollary for statistical mechanics. Suppose we are investigating the motion of molecules. We discuss the velocity of the molecule at time t as $x(t)$. If $\delta_1, \delta_2, ...\delta_n$ denote arbitrary non-overlapping time intervals, then the assumption that the paths covered by the molecule within these intervals are mutually independent is obviously equivalent to the relation (I) for given $\alpha_1, \beta_1, ...\alpha_n, \beta_n$.

It follows from Theorem 1 and 1*) that we cannot assume independence of the paths covered within the (non-overlapping) time intervals. Theorem 1*) implies that if time is partitioned into too arbitrary intervals, then the paths covered must be dependent.

On the other hand, it follows from Theorem 2), that independence of paths can be assumed, but only for time intervals chosen a priori. We can choose, e.g., an arbitrary time quantum t and divide the time interval into intervals equal to t and assume independence of paths within these intervals. Theorems 1) and 2) show by mathematical means the necessity of time quantization in statistical mathematics. Similarly the necessity of quantization of other physical magnitudes can be shown. I will note, moreover, that in statistical mechanics physicists always assume a time t, which is both finite and infinitely small as suits them better. The above theorems can be generalized in a number of ways. I have theorems referring to the existence of measures that satisfy some a priori conditions. I would gladly learn your opinion on whether my argument does indeed convince of the necessity of time quantization. Maybe you would talk about my theorems in America and write to me about the comments you might hear.

(Translated by *Wiktor Bartol*)

Załóżmy, że w E określona jest miara Lebesgua (t. zn. kompletnie addy-
tywna) spełniająca warunki

A_1) Zbiór AE ma miarę 1.

A_2) Zbiory skończone mają miarę zero

A_3) Zbiory Borela zawarte w E są mie-
rzalne.

Twierdzenie 1. Nie istnieje miara
Lebesgua spełniająca warunki (A)
i taka by zaszło

$$\text{miara } \mathcal{H}(\delta_1, \delta_2, \dots \delta_n, \alpha_1, \beta_1, \dots \alpha_n, \beta_n) = \boxed{\mathrm{I}}$$
$$= \text{miara } \mathcal{H}(\delta_1, \alpha_1, \beta_1) \cdot \text{miara } \mathcal{H}(\delta_2, \alpha_2, \beta_2) \dots \text{miara } \mathcal{H}(\delta_n, \alpha_n, \beta_n)$$

było spełnione dla każdego skończonego układu skończonego odcinków $\delta_1, \delta_2 \dots \delta_n$ nie zachodzących na siebie i dowolnych par liczb $(\alpha_1 \leq \beta_1) \dots (\alpha_n \leq \beta_n)$.

Twierdzenie 2. Do każdego układu odcinków ~~daw~~ (skończonego lub nie) $\delta_1, \delta_2, \dots \delta_n, \dots$ nie zachodzących na siebie istnieje ~~taka~~ miara Lebesgua spełniająca warunki (B)

Facsimile of the enclosure with the second letter of Stefan Banach to Stanisław Ulam (page 1)

Niech E będzie dowolny(m) *nieskończony(m)* zbiorem funkcji $x(t)$ całkowalnych w $(0 \le t \le 1)$ i spełniających warunek

$$\int_0^1 |x(t)|\, dt \le 1 \qquad (1)$$

[nie zakładamy, że zbiór E jest zbiorem wszystkich funkcji spełniających (1)] Zbiór E uważamy za zbiór metryczny przez zwykłą odległość

$$(x_1, x_2) = \int_0^1 |x_1(t) - x_2(t)|\, dt \qquad (2)$$

~~Niech~~ Jeżeli $\delta_1, \delta_2, \ldots \delta_n, \ldots$ oznacza dowolny układ *(skończony lub nie)* rozłącznych przedziałów $(0, 1)$ nie zachodzących na siebie ia: $(\alpha_1 \le \beta_1), (\alpha_2 \le \beta_2), \ldots (\alpha_n \le \beta_n), \ldots$ jest dowolnym układem par liczb rzeczywistych, to symbol

$$\mathcal{H}(\delta_1, \delta_2, \ldots \delta_n; \alpha_1, \beta_1, \alpha_2, \beta_2, \ldots \alpha_n, \beta_n \ldots)$$

oznacza zbiór tych funkcji $x(t) \in E$ dla których zachodzi

$$\alpha_i \le \int_{\delta_i} x(t)\, dt \le \beta_i, \quad i = 1, 2, \ldots n, \ldots \qquad (3)$$

i takem, że związek

miara $\mathcal{H}(\delta_1, \delta_2, \dots \delta_u, \dots \alpha_1, \beta_1, \dots \alpha_u, \beta_u, \dots) =$

$=$ miara $\mathcal{H}(\delta_1, \alpha_1, \beta_1) \cdot$ miara $\mathcal{H}(\delta_2, \alpha_2, \beta_2) \cdot \dots$

zachodzi dla każdego układu par liczb

rzeczywistych $(\alpha_1 \leq \beta_1) \dots (\alpha_u \leq \beta_u), \dots$.

<u>Uwaga</u>. Twierdzenie 1 można wypowie-

dzieć w postaci osobnej:

<u>Twierdzenie 1*)</u>. Do każdej miary

Lebesgue'a spełniającej warunek (β),

można dobrać takie $\varepsilon > 0$, że jeżeli

przedział $(0, 1)$ rozłożymy na skończenie

$\delta_1, \delta_2, \dots \delta_u$; nie zachodzące na siebie

o długościach mniejszych od $\bigotimes \varepsilon$, to

związek $(\overline{I})$ nie będzie spełniony dla

każdego układu liczb $(\alpha_1 \leq \beta_1) \dots (\alpha_u \leq \beta_u)$.

ditto (page 3)

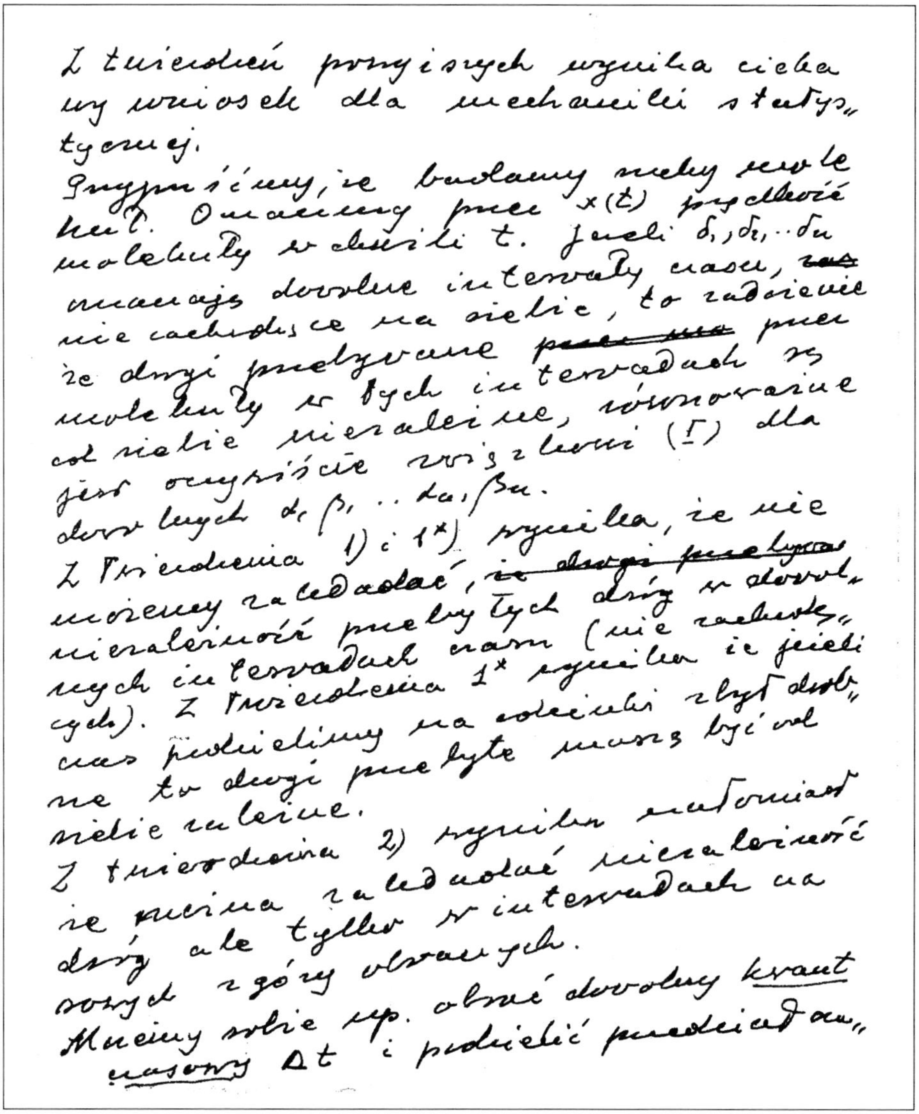
Z twierdzeń powyższych wynika ciekawy wniosek dla mechaniki statystycznej.
Przypuśćmy, że badamy ruchy molekuł. Oznaczmy przez x(t) prędkość molekuły w chwili t. Jeżeli δ1, δ2, ..δn oznaczają dowolne interwały czasu, ~~nie~~ nie zachodzące na siebie, to założenie ~~przez mo~~ przez że drogi przebyte w tych interwałach przez molekuły są od siebie niezależne, równoważne jest oczywiście równości (I) dla dowolnych α1, β1, .. αn, βn.
Z twierdzenia 1) i 1*) wynika, że nie możemy zakładać, ~~że drogi przebyte~~ niezależności przebytych dróg w dowolnych interwałach czasu (nie zachodzących). Z twierdzenia 1* wynika, że jeżeli dowolny czas podzielimy na odcinki, to drogi przebyte muszą być od siebie zależne.
Z twierdzenia 2) wynika natomiast, że można zakładać niezależność w interwałach na drogi ale tylko obranych z góry.
Możemy sobie np. obrać dowolny kwant czasowy Δt i podzielić przedział

ditto (page 4)

wszy na interwały równe Δt i
rozkładać niezależność dróg w tych
interwałach.

Twierdzenia 1) i 2) okazują, na dodze
matematycznej, konieczność kwantowania czasu w mechanice statystycznej. Pisło

Podobnie można obrać konieczność
kwantowania innych wielkości fi-
zycznych.

~~Twierdzenia podane ważne~~
Zauważ jeszcze, że w mechanice
statystycznej zawsze przyjmuje
jakiś czas Δt który jest skończony
i nieskończenie mały jak im jest
lepiej.

Twierdzenia poniższe można uogólnić,
mnucić. Mając ... Twierdzenia
odnoszące się do istnienia miar
spódnicjszych z góry zadane warunki.

Ciekawy jestem Pańskiego zdania
o tem czy rozumowanie moje prze... czasu.
książka o konieczność kwantowania
Mnie Pan opowie o tych twierdze-
niach w Ameryce i napisze mi uwagi
z jakimi się Pan spotkał.

2.4 Third letter[18] of Stefan Banach to Stanisław Ulam

Dear Staszek,[19]

I received your card and letter. I was perturbed reading about your struggles with a typhoon. Concerning the political situation in Europe we are fighting for a common border with Hungary. It looks likely that we will get one. Mazur will probably be successful in Poznań. He has been invited by Biernacki[20] to give a lecture there. He'll be discussing the theory of operations.

I am working now on additive integrable functionals. Namely, suppose there is the Lebesgue measure on the space of $\mathcal{L}^2$-sequences $\{\vartheta_i\}$, $\sum \vartheta_i^2 < \infty$. Consequently, one may discuss functionals which are additive and integrable. From this some theories follow for solving linear equations almost everywhere. Additive and integrable functionals do not have to be continuous even Baire, only they must be defined almost everywhere. The expression $\int_0^1 \alpha(t)x(t)dt$, where $x \in \mathcal{L}^2$ and $\alpha(t)$ is an arbitrary measurable function, with a good enough measure it may be an additive functional defined almost everywhere in $\mathcal{L}^2$ and Lebesgue integrable.

Besides, I have started to prepare a theory of functions of many variables. A monograph has been published in Polish on *Analytic Functions*[21] by Saks and Zygmund[22]. It's a nice book.

I am awaiting more news from you. In my next letter I will write more extensively about additive integrable functionals.

My very best wishes and embraces,
Stefan

Lvov, 27 October 1938.

---

[18]A copy of letter in the library collection of the American Philosophical Society in Philadelphia.

[19]Staszek – pet name for Stanisław (Stanislaus, Stanley).

[20]Mieczysław Biernacki (1891-1959).

[21]*Funkcje Analityczne* by Stanisław Saks and Antoni Zygmund, Monografie Matematyczne (Mathematical Monographs) vol. 10, Warsaw–Lvov–Wilno 1938; English translation: *Analytic Functions*, Monografie Matematyczne vol. 28, Warsaw–Wrocław 1952.

[22]Antoni Zygmund (1900–1992).

Kochany Stanku

Otrzymałem Twoją kartkę i
list. Z przejściem czytałem
Twoje zmagania z tajfunem.
Jeśli chodzi o sytuację poli-
tyczną w Europie to obecnie
walczymy o wspólną granicę
z Węgrami. Prawdopodobnie dosta-
niemy ją. Masur ma prawdopodobnie przejść wr. Poznaniu.
Został wyproszony na Tam
na włusyt przez Biernackiego.
Będzie miał D o drodze
operacji.
Ja pracuję obecnie nad

Facsimile of the third letter of Stefan Banach to Stanisław Ulam (page 1).

funkcjonałami addytywnymi i absolutnie ciągłemi. Chciałem mianowicie o nich naddpewniejsze: Przypuśćmy że w przerdnieniu L^2 ciągłej $\{\partial_i\}$ $\sum \partial_c^2 < \infty$ jest obecna miara Lebesgowska. Można nic mówić o funkcjonałach addytywnych i absolutnie ciągłych. Stąd rypdjynuje nową teorii o mieszaniu wersion linjowych prawie wszędzie i .p. Funkcjonały addytywne absolutnie ciągłe nie muszą być ciągłe vavet Bairowskie i nie tylko absolutnie prawie wszędzie. Wyrażenie $\int \alpha(t) K(t) \, dt$ gdzie $x \in L^2$ vaś $\alpha(t)$ dowolny funkcja mienaływ może być przy dość prostej mierze

ditto (page 2)

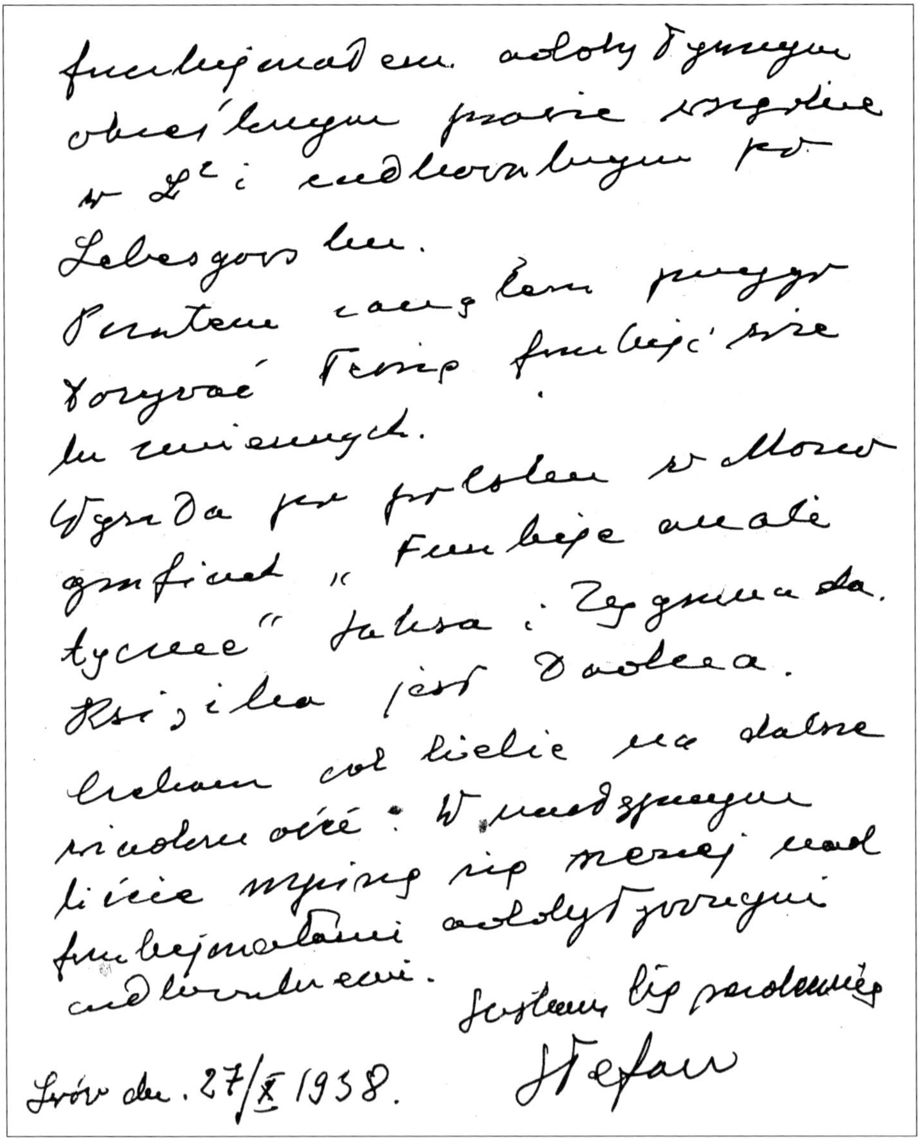
Lwów dn. 27/X 1938.

Stefan

ditto (page 3)

Panie Stasiu, jak Pan widzi i ja do-
pisuję się do tego matematycznego listu
Stefana, który na początku miał iść jako
list całkiem prywatny - osobisty, widać
stąd, że listy z ręką matematyka, muszą
tak wyglądać, że na dwa zdania prywatne
.2 twierdzenia i to się nazywa list całkiem
osobisty. - Za to naprawdę całkiem osobiście
żałuję, że bardzo nam brak Pana, nasze
ciekapady nie są już takie miłe i muszę
Panu powiedzieć, że co trzeci kieliszek
pijemy na Pana zdrowie i powodzenie,
widać, że taki platoniczny brak trójkąta
jest bardzo potrzebny i wtedy, pyszę nieraz
się pztandawiamy, czy to dowidzenia będzie
w Ameryce czy znów w Polsce. ja, jak zwy-
czajnie pyspiewuję całkiem moro skompono-
waną piosenkę, "it is a long way to
you" itd. - W każdym razie, gdzie i kiedy-
kolwiek będzie, sądzę że nam wszystkim
będzie bardzo miłe. Jak Pan że zobaczem
myślę, że już wszystko, szczęśliwie przeminęło
i wraca Pan do dawnej formy. - Bardzo
Pana proszę pisać nie czekając listów
Stefana, bo on do pisania jest taki
ciężki, nawet jeśli chodzi o najmilsze

ditto (page 4)

Dear Stasiu,[23]

As you can see, I am writing an addition to Stefan's letter about mathematics, which started out as quite a private and personal one, but it seems that when a mathematician writes then for two personal words there will also be 2 mathematics proofs, and that is supposed to be a strictly personal letter! Well, I am writing to say, really strictly personally, that we miss you very much. Our outings now are not as much fun, and I want to tell you that every third drink we have is a toast to your health and success. It looks as if such a third platonic side of a triangle is very necessary and nice. We often wonder whether when we see you again it will be in America or in Poland, as I sometimes sing the recently composed: "It is a long way to you", etc. In any case, I'm sure that wherever it happens to be it will be a very nice occasion for all of us. How is your health? I trust that everything has now passed happily and that you are returning to your earlier form. Please write without waiting for Stefan's letters because he is always so slow to write even to those who are closest and dearest.

> Stefan Jr[24] and I enclose our very sincere greetings.
> Łucja Banach[25]

> (Translated by *John Greczek* and *Wiktor Bartol*)

2.5 Letter[26] of Stefan Greczek[27] to Stefan Banach

Krakow, 30/10, 1943

In answer to your letter of the 21 st. of this month:
   The fourth commandment of God is: "Honor your father and your mother, that your days may be long and that you may prosper".
   This is not limited to having to honor only some but all parents.
   How did you honor me in this letter? You did not write dearest father, or father, or anything.

---

[23]Stasiu – another pet name for Stanisław.
[24]See biographical note B-3.
[25]Łucja Banach (1897–1954) née Braus, wife of Stefan Banach.
[26]A copy of a rough draft manuscript provided by Alicja Żuraniewska from the Greczek family archives.
[27]Stefan Greczek (1867–1967) – father of Stefan Banach.

Facsimile of the rough draft of a letter of Stefan Greczek
to Stefan Banach (page 1 only).

According to the revelation of St. John, nations and generations will form separate groups in heaven so that each nation constitutes a separate group, as on earth, and worships God in the language it used here.

When it comes time that you go to heaven, you will not go to the Italians, or Spaniards, or the French, or English or Germans – but only to the Poles, and amongst them the call of your blood will lead you to the generation of Greczeks. Differences in birth do not count there any longer. Your wife and your son will also accompany you to our family. I have hope in God that my whole family is already there: parents, brothers, sisters, nieces and more distant relatives, also our ancestors.

We are only on earth for a short time but there for eternity. No one is happy here, even rich people feel unhappy because they are always lacking something. Everyone must suffer. Some must endure more suffering than others.

The matter of your birth is as follows:

When you were born I was 24 years and 4 months old. I was serving in the army. Without permission from the military authorities I was not allowed to marry. Permission was only granted to those who were able to document and show that the marriage would improve their means and circumstances. Your mother, who was a maid by trade, was paid only 5 Fl.[28] per month. It was out of the question to even think about getting permission to marry. With my income neither could I provide for your mother. After a month we decided to give you up to be raised in the country and I pledged to pay for you, which I did every month.

Your mother took work as a nanny for which she received 8 Fl. per month. After several months when a woman brought you to Krakow to show (your mother) that you were alive and well, fate decreed that your mother took her to the house of your (future) foster mother[29] because she (your mother) worked close by. Your foster mother declared that she would be willing to take you in, to bring you up and care for you, without any payment, to which your birth mother agreed. And so she took you from the woman and handed you to your new guardian.

So now with nothing in your mother's way she met a certain young man, who was serving his third year in the army and, after being discharged and obtaining employment on the railways, he married her. From that time on your mother no longer worried about you and she later had other children.

Your foster mother, a noble and good woman, who had no children of her

---

[28] Austro-Hungarian gulden.
[29] Franciszka Płowa.

own, raised you and loved you like her own child. With a no-good husband, who she knew would not provide for her when she became elderly and could no longer work, she did not want to become a burden on society. That is why she took in a niece and you to bring up believing that one of you would give her shelter in her old age. However, she was never a burden to anyone because she was taken early by God.

Your foster mother was proud of you. You were a healthy and attractive child. Mien,[30] the photographer, took pictures of you in different poses and these served for his advertisements. People would stop at his exhibition and admire the beautiful child. As a result of that Mien became famous around town. All the ladies came to him to be photographed and to have their children photographed. In the meantime you were growing up and after 6 years you went to school. You were a good student and every year advanced to a higher level until you completed grammar school. Your mother, with chest puffed out, was delighted that her Stefek[31] was such a good student. As I watched your upbringing I saw no reason to interfere and give your mother advice, because everything was progressing as it should. You were provided an excellent living standard because your mother took such good care of you. Your clothes, shoes, underwear, were always of the best quality. Textbooks you also had. If your mother had neglected you, did not take care of you and did not send you to school, be assured, I would have taken you to my house and sent you to attend school. But your mother did that on my behalf. Such was the will of God Almighty and He would most certainly have credited her with this good deed.

At the time of your high school graduation (your) mother said to me: you have to provide Stefek with a nice suit for his graduation. And so, you and I went to see a tailor, you chose the material, the tailor measured you and in a week's time the suit was ready. I paid a sum of 100 crowns for the suit. That was a lot of money at the time. I could have taken you to a Jewish tailor and bought a ready-made suit for 20 crowns, because that is what ready-made suits cost. But I did not do so, because honor would not allow that.

It's not right, therefore, to complain that you spent your young years with strangers, and not with your parents, because your life with them was good. For that the Lord God gave you health, good looks and a gift for study, and from your parents you received good blood. You could be an example of what the Greeks considered to be the ideal: "the cultural ideal of

---

[30] Juliusz Mien (1842–1905).

[31] Stefek – pet name for Stefan (Stephen/Steven).

the ancient Greeks was the person who was physically beautiful and morally good".

A memory that has been preserved in our family is that our ancestors were Greeks. During some war between Poland and Wallachia (currently part of Romania) in the seventeenth century, three brothers, young Greek knights, found themselves as prisoners of the Poles. At that time there were no prisoner exchanges. They were transferred to the King's lodge in Podhale and later they settled in Ostrowsko. A son of one of the brothers emigrated to Bucharest and remained there.

I will briefly contrast for you the life of Waksmundzki,[32] husband of Tośka.[33]   For 8 years he would walk to grammar school from Waksmund to Nowy Targ, a distance of 4 km. He had to do it regardless if there was rain, foul weather, heavy frost, or a snow storm. After graduating from grammar school he completed a year of military service. Then he enrolled at university. During his time at the university he received no help from his parents, despite the fact they were able to afford it, and he had to support himself through tutoring.

He sustained himself by eating plain bread and drinking tea without sugar because he didn't have enough money for anything more, and a lunch cost 45 groszy. If he was not able to pay for his university dormitory they would take away his bed linen and he would have to sleep on bare boards until such time as he paid the rent, which was 16 zlotys.

Moreover, he had to make sure he paid the tuition fees and had to think about textbooks, which he would obtain from England, and he also had to think about his clothes.

After completing his university studies and passing the examination for a master's degree his lot improved because he was appointed an Assistant with a salary of 100 zlotys per month. Once he had the position of Assistant he thought about getting married. But with his salary he was unable to support a wife. It happened that he met Tośka. Therefore, I undertook and promised to support him and his wife until such time as he became a docent,[34] or obtained industrial employment. As a result they married and lived with me. Tośka became the lady of the house. He gained a doctorate in chemistry as a married man.

You might think that Waksmundzki bore a grudge against his parents that they did not help him during his university studies. Absolutely not.

---

[32]See biographical note B-22.

[33]Tośka – pet name for Antonina (Antoinette).

[34]Docent – an academic title in Poland immediately below that of a full professor. It is equivalent to *Privatdozent* in Germany or to an associate professor in the USA.

It is accepted in the country that, with the exception of medical studies, a student must support himself while at university.

What a big difference there is between you and him. You experienced no want, spent your young years without worry, and had everything that you needed. Waksmundzki, on the other hand, lived his early years in want and hunger, although his parents were well-to-do.

> Finishing, I send my love to you and your wife.
> Sincerely, your father,
> Stefan Greczek

> (Translated by *John Greczek*)

2.6 Letter[35] of Stanisław Ulam to Roman Kałuża[36]

July 14, 1980

Dear Dr. Kałuża,

Just received your letter and chapter [37] on Banach and do not need to tell you how grateful I am. I do hope you can send me the whole book.

I am writing this in English since it is difficult to dictate in Polish and my handwriting, I have been told, is quite undecipherable.

You have performed miraculous work. It must have taken incredible detective work, ingenuity and sense to do it so successfully. I am very eager to see the rest.

There are very many anecdotes, impressions and remarks about and by him which I remember. Despite our 17 years difference in age I felt that there was a deep friendship between us which developed between us after I met him in 1929, I believe at the Polytechnical Institute where he was giving some lectures.

From the beginning I felt great admiration for his mind and I noticed a couple of years later that he seemed to like my mathematical attitudes and me personally too. In fact, when sometime later he was experiencing

---

[35] A copy of letter in the library collection of the American Philosophical Society in Philadelphia.

[36] See bibliographical note B-11

[37] Ulam refers to the first chapter of the manuscript of the Stefan Banach biography [19] by Roman Kałuża, first published in Polish in 1992.

strained relations with some of his colleagues (due to financial difficulties
and the fact that the department made an arrangement to manage his
monthly salary), Banach, his wife and I went together to the restaurants
Szkowron and *Atlas* literally dozens of times. I was very proud of the distinction of being the only friend with them on these occasions.

I admired his mathematical remarks and ideas during our daily sessions
at the *Café Szkocka*[38]. By the way, a big book in English containing the
translation of the *Scottish Book*, which I made some thirty years ago,[39] and
an enormous number of commentaries by many mathematicians is now finished and about to be published[40]. It was edited by Professor Dan Mauldin
from the University of North Texas in Denton Texas. It will be quite a mon-
umental affair and a great tribute to Banach.

He said once that working on proofs is what interested him sometimes
the most about mathematical creativity. But he credited me for having
special foresight and intuition in presenting the new problems.

$$[...]^{41}$$

---

[38]Scottish Café.

[39]See Ref. [38].

[40]Ulam refers to Ref. [26] edited by R. Daniel Mauldin.

[41]Unfortunately, the other pages of the letter are missing from the library collection.

Chapter 3

Recollections

3.1 Stefan Banach Jr about his Father

An interview[1] with Stefan Banach Jr[2]
conducted by Piotr Hajłasz

Stefan Banach Jr is a doctor of medicine and a neurosurgeon. In connection with the centennial of his father's birth we asked him to grant *Delta* an interview.

Q: *When reading various biographies of your father one can find certain inconsistencies.*
A: The majority of the biographical data concerning my father, wherever it may be found, has come from me. However, before it was committed to writing, someone would frequently change something and/or add something with the result that the written information is incorrect. For example, my father was born in 1892, on 30 March not on 20 March, as has been stated numerous times. Where did this mistake come from? It was given in error by Steinhaus during a speech he gave honoring my father, and then it was repeated by others. Steinhaus also stated that after he was born my father was given up to be raised by a laundrywoman by the name of Banach, and supposedly because of gratitude to her he adopted her surname. That is quite false. The laundrywoman to whom he was given to be raised was Franciszka Płowa, whereas Banach was his mother's surname.

---

[1] Translation of an article from *Delta* (No. 10 (221), pp. 1–4, 1992). Reproduced here with the kind permission of the editorial office.

[2] See biographical note B-3.

Q: *You said that you are writing your own recollections of your father. Would you be able to provide some details?*
A: The writing of these recollections is only now in progress, and they will be published sometime, God willing.

Q: *It is a known fact that as a child your father spoke French fluently. Steinhaus writes that it is not known when he learned it.*
A: But it is known. As I already mentioned, my father was placed with Franciszka Płowa to be raised by her. Her daughter, whom Banach looked on as a sister, 15 years older than him, had a friend, Juliusz Mien, who was a photographer in Krakow. He was French and spoke French with my father. That is where his fluent French came from. Incidentally, Juliusz Mien specialized in children's photographs and almost all of the surviving photographs of my father from his childhood were taken by him.

Q: *What were your father's circumstances like during his childhood?*
A: To help his foster mother he began to tutor, initially in all subjects but then only mathematics and, finally, he tutored only students who were preparing for their high school diploma ("matura") examinations. In time his foster mother and niece – both were laundrywomen – prospered and were able to open their own laundry, which employed 15 to 20 workers. Naturally, my father's circumstances improved after that.

Q: *On another occasion you mentioned that when he was a student your father was a dancer in an opera.*
A: When he was a student he danced the "Mazurek", as the second couple in the opera "Halka", for which he earned 20 hallers.[3] In another opera he was one of six porters who had to carry a bull on the stage.

Q: *Was he interested in sports?*
A: As a boy he was a dedicated football player. He played in the Błonie Park in Krakow. During his student days he was very good and keen on billiards. But billiards then was different than today's. It was called *karambol*, and sometimes *karambolka*. Only three balls were involved. Now American billiards is fashionable. That is something quite different. He was a very good tennis player. And as he was left-handed this caused additional difficulties for an opponent. It's more difficult to play against a left-hander because he plays a little differently from what we are used to. I learned to play tennis from him. Incidentally, although he was left-handed he wrote with his right hand – in those days schools required each student to use his

---

[3]Haller or heller – an Austro-Hungarian coin valued at 1/100 of a krone (crown).

right hand when writing. He wrote with his right but whenever he threw a stone he would use his left – you can always tell a left-hander that way.

Q: *Was he interested in politics? What were his views?*
A: Yes, he was. However, any short answer to your second question would cause you to misunderstand his views. In those days the political situation was so complex that it's simply not possible to give a short answer to this question. One thing I can say. He was absolutely not a communist.

Q: *Did he fit the common perception of what a university professor should be like?*
A: I remember when once he came to my high school for a conference. My school friends were surprised that he did not have a long beard and was not a shaky old man. That was the expectation then of what a university professor should be like. To the contrary, he was a young man and did not conform to the various accepted norms. In the 1930s it was unheard of for someone to walk around with his shirt collar unbuttoned and wide open. You had to have your shirt buttoned up and wear a tightly tied necktie. You had to wear a waistcoat under your jacket. You also had to have gloves that, if you were not actually wearing them, had to be held in your hand. Father broke that mode. I remember, for instance, when one time he went out wearing what was at that time an unfashionable short-sleeved shirt and sporting a walking stick. These de rigueur dress codes began later to change slowly.

Q: *How did you spend your vacations?*
A: My school breaks lasted two months. I would spend July in Boy Scout Camp and August with my parents in the East Carpathian Mountains.

Q: *Was your father involved with mathematics during the WWII occupation?*
A: He was involved with mathematics every day, for all practical purposes without a break, until the end of his life. Likewise during the occupation. He was very good at multi-tasking. He was able to work under any circumstances. He was quite happy working amid the noise and bustle of a coffee-house.

Q: *Did he talk much about mathematics at home?*
A: No, he did not. Once my mother and I retired for the day, and the house was quiet, he would begin to work and continued until quite late into the night till about 3 a.m. I would like to state, however, that he always had plenty of time for me. Sundays belonged to me. Every second Sunday we went to see football matches that were played by *Pogoń Lvov.*[4] On alternate

---

[4] *Pogoń Lvov* was one of the first Polish professional sport clubs and the second oldest

I already knew when I was just a few years old that my grandmother had lost her parents early in her life, and that she was then brought up in the home of her aunt Frania.[9] I knew that Stefek also lived there at that time but I did not know why. I discerned some kind of mystery connected with his origins which Grandmother kept even from me. In the 1950s Grandmother and I visited Stefan Greczek in Ostrowsko, near Nowy Targ, while we were vacationing there at the same time as he was. She never mentioned any connection between him, his family, and Stefek. However, I began to suspect that Stefan Greczek was Stefek's father, but I did not know who his mother was. I have to admit this was a strange situation. Grandmother resolutely kept the mystery of Stefek's origins until her death. It was only in 1968, after her death, that my father told me about Stefan Banach's mother.

According to him Katarzyna Banach came to aunt Frania's house about 1890-91. She came to work in the laundry that my aunt owned. When it became apparent that she was pregnant my aunt wanted to send her home but Katarzyna insisted that in her condition, or later with a child, she dare not show herself in her village. She also revealed who the child's father was. After a baby son was born she left him in the care of aunt Frania. She herself went back to her village and shortly thereafter married a railway worker. She never had any further contact with her son. On the other hand, Stefan Greczek was a frequent visitor in aunt Frania's and my grandmother's home. My mother related to me that they had all known each other before the child was born. That was the secret that my grandmother kept. Stefek treated aunt Frania's and later my grandmother's home as his own and reciprocated our feelings for him. These strong bonds between him and my family existed throughout his whole life.

In 1913 Grandmother visited him in Lvov. Whenever he was in Krakow he would always come to see Grandmother, first by himself and later on with his son. I know that when he was in Krakow, either before or after the war, Stefan Jr stayed for a time with Grandmother. I came to know him better during the 1980s and 1990s when he was often in Krakow trying to arrange for his father's remains to be transferred to the vault reserved for famous Poles in St. Stanislaus Church in Krakow. During our meetings he would always stress that I am a part of his closest family. These were for me pleasant words even if spoken perhaps only out of respect.

I must add, for the sake of truthfulness, that there was one flaw in our relations with Stefek's family. This concerned the relation between my grandmother and his wife. I would describe it as cool. I do not think she

---

[9]Frania – pet name for Franciszka (Frances) Płowa.

Identity Card of Franciszka Płowa.

Obituary notice of the death of Franciszka Płowa.

Identity Card of Maria Puchalska.

Maria Puchalska

Maria Puchalska

ever visited Grandmother in her home. I regret that I no longer remember more and that I did not write down all of Grandmother's and Father's stories about our beloved Stefek.

Krakow, November 2007   *Maria Sowińska*
                            Granddaughter of Maria Puchalska

                            (Translated by *John Greczek*)

3.3   John J. Greczek[10] about Stefan Banach

Stefan Banach was my father Wilhelm Greczek's half-brother, and he was five years older than my father. As an adolescent after World War II and living with my parents in Great Britain, I remember my father often speaking about my uncle Stefan whom he recalled with obvious pride and affection. He also related the facts, as he knew them from his father (my grandfather) Stefan Greczek, concerning Stefan Banach's early childhood, his mother Katarzyna and the circumstances that at the time made it impossible for her and my grandfather to be married. As recounted by my father, Grandfather Stefan instead took the most honourable action possible in agreeing with Banach's mother that they should separate, so that she might return to her village and not be exposed, and for him to take sole charge of and responsibility for the child. In this respect, as with all the other details provided (see Section 3.4) by my cousin Professor Monika Hajnos-Waksmundzka concerning the subsequent relationship between Banach and his father, I am able to closely agree with what I remember hearing from my father. After the war my father was not able to return to Poland and together with my mother they spent the remainder of their lives in Great Britain. During that time they had infrequent contact with my cousin Monika's family and very limited opportunity to share information relating to Stefan Banach, who was by that time deceased. My reaction, therefore, on first reading Monika's independent account was a pleasant surprise as to how closely it corresponded to what I knew from my father. I am now excited that hopefully the record of these early days can at last be set straight to show our grandfather in a deservedly much better light as compared to, and in contrast with, what has appeared in several articles about Banach. These articles castigate him as someone who was uncaring and without feeling for the child and his mother, and as having abandoned them both. On the

---

[10]See biographical note B-10.

contrary, the opposite is true. For example, I believe it was very characteristic of him, following the seizure in 1939 of my parents' house by the Nazi
authorities, and after my father had been forced to flee the country, to immediately take my mother and me to live with him, despite his rather small
apartment in Krakow (at 4 Bonerowska Street), and we were welcomed to
remain there throughout the war years. And, even as a young boy at that
time, I remember him as a devout Christian and a caring and principled
person whom my mother and I always looked up to with love and respect.

A few years after Stefan Banach's birth Grandfather married my grandmother Helena (née Alfus) . Together they had only one child, my father
Wilhelm Stefan, born in Krakow on 15 January 1897. Within a few years
they separated and Grandmother went to live in Vienna taking my father
with her. Sometime later Grandfather obtained legal custody of my father,
who then returned to Krakow to be with him. It was during these years
that Banach and my father spent a lot of time together and related as
brothers. Anecdotes that my father used to tell of that time included that
Banach tutored and helped him with mathematics, that they both liked to
play football, and that they looked so much alike that sometimes family
friends and acquaintances had difficulty telling them apart. I understand
that during the years before the war Banach would visit us from time to
time in Krakow, but I was a young child at the time. I have no recollec-
tion of those visits. During the war, and with my father having already
left Poland, I understand my mother and I had only limited contact with
Banach, and I myself do not remember seeing him during that time. I do
recall, however, that my mother was very upset when she told me she had
been notified of his death – in 1945.

Other family details

The following is some additional information, not directly related to and not
apropos of Banach, however, I would nevertheless like to provide it. With
Banach's increasing world-wide fame more details will perhaps be searched
out and more distant family connections documented, and those facts too
should be accurately rendered.

Grandfather Stefan was very close to us throughout all the years we were
in Poland, and corresponded with us regularly in Great Britain after the
war. He died a few months short of reaching 100 years of age while still
in the same apartment in Krakow. Grandmother Helena visited and was
in frequent contact with my parents before the war and then corresponded
with us often when we were in Britain. She remarried and lived with her

second husband in Czechoslovakia until her death there in the mid-1950s. While my parents missed her, and often spoke about her in warm terms, as an older boy I do not recall that either one of them ever spoke to me about her marriage to my grandfather. It was, I always thought, something they perhaps did not know very much about.

My father Wilhelm Stefan attended the Jagiellonian University in Krakow to study law and served in the Polish army as a captain in the Polish-Bolshevik War. He was later a high-ranking director of the Polish Railways for the Katowice region. In 1939, he had to leave Poland and made his way to France where, at Coetquidan, he joined the re-created Polish army commanded by General Stanisław Maczek, which was subsequently dispatched to protect the Scottish coastline and came under British command. Later during the war my father was on the staff of the Polish Military Staff College near Peebles, in Scotland, with the rank of major.

My mother and I arrived in Great Britain shortly after the war. I received most of my schooling there, studied chemical engineering and graduated with a Ph.D. degree from the University of London in 1965. I have been in the USA since 1966 with my wife Muriel (née Millar) and our two sons Steven (Stefan) and Colin. My father died in 1971 and my mother Justyna (née Nakielna) died in 1990.

26 October 2006   *John J. Greczek*
River Forest, Illinois, USA

3.4 Alicja Żuraniewska[11] about Stefan Greczek

Following in the footsteps of my cousins Monika Waksmundzka-Hajnos[12] and John Greczek,[13] I also wish to add my recollections of our grandfather Stefan Greczek.

When I was born he was already 76 years old. We lived in Krakow at 4 Bonerowska Street. It happened that Stefan Banach Jr[14] was also staying there with us at that time and became my godfather.

Grandfather Stefan was a charming man. He was a devout Roman Catholic, possessed of a strong faith that was almost as simple and trustful as that of a child. He retained his always sharp and clear mind even to the end of his days when he was 100. I have also provided a photograph

---

[11]See biographical note B-25.
[12]See biographical note B-21.
[13]See biographical note B-10.
[14]See biographical note B-3

of Joseph (Józef) Greczek, Stefan Banach's grandfather. He came from the highlands and is seen wearing a sheepskin jacket, common attire of the highlanders. Our family tradition has always held, however, that we were descended from the Greeks. Grandfather Stefan recalled that his father's older brother spoke Greek with his children when they were growing up, and required them to answer in the same language. All the members of the Greczek family lived long lives. My great grandfather, Joseph Greczek, died in Krakow at the age of 86. Grandfather Stefan's brother, Joseph Greczek, a grammar school teacher, also died at an advanced age in Lvov long after World War II.

Grandfather always maintained a very healthful lifestyle. He exercised every morning, counting in German the way he had been taught and became accustomed to while serving in the Austrian army. The only bread he would eat was from whole wheat. He took milk with his tea. He smoked a pipe whose pleasant aromatic smell permeated the room.

It is possible to think that had Stefan Banach not been such a heavy cigarette smoker he too would have enjoyed a long life. Grandfather was always very healthy. Unfortunately, he suffered a fall when he was 99 that resulted in a torn knee meniscus. This immobilised him and caused numerous circulation problems that ultimately led to his death. I arranged for him to be interred at the Rakowicki Cemetery in the sepulcher of his father Joseph, his wife Albina (née Adamska) and his son Bolesław, who died at the young age of 22 while a law student. If not for the misfortune of his accident, Grandfather may have lived to an age well beyond 100. All of his vital organs were healthy, and he was not missing a single tooth.

Since none of his friends were still alive, I had expected very few mourners (besides family members) to attend his funeral, but I was surprised to see a sizeable crowd. These were all the many people who had known and liked him, and who had come to pay their last respects. Grandfather was well liked because he was always calm and in control of himself. He was also generous and charming, especially in his dealings with women. He was kind and had a pleasant manner. He had a full head of hair that was white as snow. He worked hard all his life to support his large family. In addition to working for the city tax office he had also worked as an accountant for the finest hotel in Krakow, the Grand Hotel on Sławkowska Street. He had also been employed as an accountant at the best restaurant of that time, the Żywiec, as well as at several other local firms and institutions. My grandmother, Albina Adamska, was originally from Lvov.

Among grandfather's papers I came across a handwritten draft of a 1943 letter to his son, Professor Stefan Banach, which I enclose. As his father, he always provided for Stefan Banach's welfare to the best of his means and abilities. The young Stefan's guardian, Franciszka Płowa, was a well-to-do lady who was very fond of and took good care of him. Stefan Banach Jr related how he had only once seen his father cry and that was when he was told that she had died. I remember visiting her with grandfather when I was a child. Her house was very well appointed and there were many impressive paintings on the walls. Several years later I visited there again and was given photographs of Stefan Banach, which I subsequently gave to Stefan Banach Jr. Among these was the charming photograph, shown on the Stefan Banach website, of the little Stefan sleeping on a bench in the Planty Gardens in Krakow. A photo portrait of Stefan Banach remained in Franciszka Płowa's house, and I would imagine it is still in the possession of her family.

The name Stefan has continued to be faithfully preserved in our family in remembrance of our grandfather Stefan Greczek.

I loved my grandfather very much and would hope that his memory would be respected.

Krakow, 24 January 2007 *Alicja Żuraniewska*
(Translated by *John Greczek*)

3.5 Monika Waksmundzka-Hajnos[15] about Stefan Greczek

I would like to provide additional information and set the record straight concerning the person of Stefan Greczek, the father of Stefan Banach. Reading about him in various papers and articles about his famous son, one can come away with an inaccurate, or even quite false, impression regarding his descent, financial and family situation.

Stefan Greczek was born in November 1867, in the small village of Ostrowsko, situated in the Dunajec River valley near the Tatra Mountains in southern Poland. He was the first-born son of Joseph and Antonina, who were poor farmers. He had four younger brothers and sisters. As a young boy he helped graze cattle and sheep and helped to look after his parents' small farm. He attended elementary schools in Ostrowsko and in the nearby small town of Nowy Targ, but was unable to continue his education there

---

[15]See biographical note B-21.

because at that time Nowy Targ did not have a grammar school. His family did not have the financial means to send him for further education. Consequently, as a mere youth barely in his teens, he set off in search of work in Budapest, which at that time was a favourite and common destination for many young people from the same largely agricultural area of Poland. Some went to escape difficult conditions, and all went looking to improve their economic prospects. His journey to Budapest (a distance of more than 250 kilometers) was entirely on foot walking the whole way in the company of several other young teenagers from his village. Since Stefan Greczek already had good reading and writing skills at that time, and as he was talented, he soon learned German. He was thus able to obtain a position working in an office. Commenting about that later, one of his group, who had journeyed with him to Budapest, is noted to have said "all the rest of us to the shovel, Stefan to an office!"

His office position did not last long, however, because he was soon conscripted into the Austrian army. Once in the army, and as a young soldier, he met a young girl, a countrywoman from the same area of Poland that he was from, Katarzyna Banach. Although he himself never spoke much about her, it has always been understood by the family that she was employed as a maid or servant to the same officer whom Stefan was assigned to as an orderly. They fell in love. The fruit of that love was born on 30 March 1892. Stefan was then 24 years old. The young father would have no hope or realistic chance at that time for a better future other than to remain in the army. At his rank he was forbidden to marry without permission. Those who did were immediately discharged. In a letter to his son Stefan Banach, on 10 October 1943, he writes[16]:

> When you were born I was 24 years and 3 months old. I was serving in the army, without permission from the military authorities I was not allowed to marry. Permission was only granted to those who were able to document and show that the marriage would improve their means and circumstances (...) It was out of the question for me to even think about getting permission to marry.

Suffice to say the young couple decided to separate. For a time Katarzyna went to live in Krakow. She subsequently married a railway worker and is known to have later left Krakow. Her whereabouts after that time are unknown. Before they parted the young father made two promises to Katarzyna – that he would look after and take care of the child, whom they christened Stefan, until he was of full age, and that he would never reveal that she was his mother. He kept those promises. And, while it

---

[16]See Section 2.5.

would have been easier to commit the child to an orphanage, he assumed full care and responsibility for him.

There is information that at that point the child was taken to Ostrowsko to be looked after there by Stefan Sr's mother, Antonina. This was not just some "older lady", as some writers have stated, but in fact the now elderly Greczek matriarch, Stefan Banach's grandmother, who lived with family members in a very small cottage, typical of many others in that region – often called *chicken huts*. Unfortunately, some time after that she became ill. Now she herself and little Stefan both needed to be cared for. It is noteworthy at that point that, even although she had several other children, Antonina preferred to go and live with her son Stefan, now in Krakow, and she spent the remainder of her years there with him. Because of his mother's poor health, Stefan Sr (with the full knowledge of Katarzyna Banach) decided to place the little boy Banach with the owner of a laundry business in Krakow, a well-to-do lady, not a washerwoman as has appeared in some articles about Stefan Banach. Even though she was prosperous Stefan Sr paid her regularly for the upkeep of his son. This continued for an extended period until Banach was of an age to be able to leave to go to Lvov to study. In a letter to his son Stefan Greczek indexGreczek, Stefan writes:

> *Your foster mother, a noble and good woman, who had no children of her own, raised you and loved you like her own child.*

In due time Stefan Greczek became a revenue service official, and later an accountant, and even though he had not received much formal education and was practically self-taught, he was always known in Krakow as *Pan Radca*, i.e., *Counsellor* during the time following World War I. His own family life, however, was not that easy. His first wife Helena and he separated after a few years of marriage. One child, a son Wilhelm, was born of that marriage. After they separated Helena took the child to live with her in Vienna but following lengthy court proceedings there he gained custody of Wilhelm, who then returned to live with him in Krakow. Ultimately his first wife remarried. At around the turn of the century Stefan Greczek met Albina Adamska, a young lady from a family of merchants in Lvov. He obviously possessed a lot of personal charm that, despite his somewhat checkered past, she became very attached to him. Their union resulted in four children: Kazimierz, Tadeusz, Bolesław and Antonina. However, Stefan and Albina had to wait for 20 years before they could be legally married, and before she and the children were entitled to use Greczek as their surname. Stefan Greczek never lost contact with the Podhale region where he came from, and always vacationed there with his family. It was there that, on the site of his family's old small cottage, a new large house was built in 1930. It was an impressive storied building of wooden 1 og construction. The enjoyment it brought was, however, shortly marred by the death of his wife Albina in 1935, preceded by the premature death at a young age of their son Bolesław. Then in 1936 heavy flooding badly damaged the new house.

Antonina Greczek, daughter of Stefan Greczek, had knowledge of Banach, but only as being a family friend. She was 25 years younger than him. That he was in fact her brother, her beloved father's son, she only found out in 1939. At the outbreak of World War II Antonina, her husband and father Stefan, set off from Krakow in panic and confusion and headed in the direction of Nowy Korczyn. There they became separated and Antonina and her father continued on their own towards Lvov. Once there, with aunts and uncles from her mother's side of the family, Antonina met Stefan Banach for the first time. It was only then she discovered that he was her half-brother. This was a shock and she did not understand how it was she had not known, and why her father had not told her. He calmed her down and explained the circumstances and the difficulties that e xisted at the time of the Austro-Hungarian rule if someone wanted to register a child born out of wedlock as his own, and how his father realized there were very few good options available to him, and that there was not much he could do. Antonina and Stefan Banach quickly became friends, and confided in and loved each other as brother and sister.

Even though I was born five years after his death, I grew up in our family home very much aware and conscious of the atmosphere of love and strong affection for Stefan Banach, and I remember well my mother's legendary stories about him, especially about their first meeting. Memories of him are very vivid to this day even though my mother died four years ago.

My grandfather Stefan Greczek survived to be 100 and worked as the administrator of the tenement building he lived in until he was 90 years old. Two years prior to his death he even spent a vacation in Ostrowsko. His house is still there, built on the same site as the small cottage where Stefan Banach spent the first period of his life as a child.

Lublin, 12 September 2006   *Monika Wakmundzka-Hajnos*
                                                (Translated by *John Greczek*)

Józef Greczek, father of Stefan Greczek.

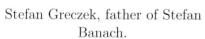

Stefan Greczek, father of Stefan Banach.

Stefan Greczek.

Stefan Greczek.

Identity Card of Stefan Greczek.

Diploma of Emperor Franz Joseph I awarded to Stefan Greczek.

The children of Stefan Greczek. From the left: Antonina Greczek, Wilhelm S. Greczek, Justyna Greczek (wife of Wilhelm), Tadeusz Greczek, 1935.

Antonina Greczek, c. 1938.

Wilhelm S. Greczek at about 24 years of age. Photograph taken c. 1921.

Descendants of Stefan Greczek and Stefan Banach

Children of Stefan Greczek:

1. Stefan – a professor of mathem atics.
2. Wilhelm – a student of law at the Jagiellonian University; a director, before World War II, of the Polish National Railways (PKP) in the Katowice district.
3. Kazimierz – Ph.D. in law.
4. Tadeusz – M.D.
5. Bolesław – died at the age of 21, student of law.
6. Antonina – M.Sc. in pharmacy.

Grandchildren of Stefan Greczek:

1. Stefan Banach Jr[17] – son of Stefan – Ph.D. in medicine.
2. John J. Greczek[18] – son of Wilhelm – Ph.D. in chemistry/thermodynamics (received in England).
3. Alicja Żuraniewska [19] née Greczek – daughter of Tadeusz – LLM solicitor.
4. Monika Waksmundzka-Hajnos[20] – daughter of Antonina née Greczek – Ph.D. in chemistry, Ph.D. and habilitation in pharmacy, professor of Academy of Medicine.

Grandchildren of Stefan Banach – daughters of Stefan Banach Jr and Alina Filipowicz-Banach [21]

1. Iwona Banach-Suchowierska (née Banach) – alumna of Warsaw University, doctor of applied linguistics.
2. Kasia Banach-Salas (née Banach) – registered homeopath.

Grandchildren of Stefan Banach Jr:

1. Joachim Stefan Suchowierski – son of Iwona Banach-Suchowierska ,
2,3. Georgia and Audrey Salas – daughters of Kasia Banach-Salas.

---

[17]See biographical note B-3.
[18]See biographical note B-10.
[19]See biographic note B-25.
[20]See biographical note B-21.
[21]See biographical note B-9.

3.6   Andrzej Alexiewicz about Stefan Banach

Andrzej Alexiewicz's[22] **conversations with Stefan Banach from the *Lvovian Notebook* recollected by Władysław Alexiewicz.**[23]

In my father Andrzej Alexiewicz's progress report at the Jan Kazimierz University in Lvov there is a record of the subjects he took with Professor Stefan Banach. In the academic year 1935/36, when my father was a first-year physics student, these were classes on analytical geometry that continued for three trimesters and a course on set theory.

It is worth noting the somewhat unusual situation: Banach, Full Professor, conducted these classes as supplementary exercises to the course taught by Stefan Kaczmarz, an associate professor at that time.

Later my father gave up his physics studies to study for a degree in mathematics. In his third year he attended two courses given by Stefan Banach: *Differential and integral calculus* (part II) and *Introduction to the theory of real functions*.

In his later years of studies the student was expected to take two fundamental courses: *Theory of real functions* and *Theory of operators* in the fourth year. During the last year, already at the time of the first Soviet occupation, my father attended Professor Banach's seminars and lectures on the *Theory of Operators* and *Ballistic Problems*.

The *List of Lectures for the Academic Year 1939/40* at the Jan Kazimierz University in Lvov, reproduced in the Appendix in the part concerning mathematics, is breathtaking. One could only wish to have the opportunity to attend lectures by such famous people! After earning his master's degree my father worked in Banach's department as an assistant during the time of both Soviet occupations. One of his young colleagues at that time was Zygmunt Zahorski, then M.Sc. My father was also one of those who, together with the cream of the Lvov intelligentsia, worked as a lice feeder at Professor Rudolf Weigl's famous institute. Nevertheless, in May 1944, he managed to successfully defend his Ph.D. thesis on "Sequences of Operations" in the then underground Jan Kazimierz University. His thesis advisor was Professor Władysław Orlicz.

In my father's thin notebook I came across several pages written by him with the heading *Conversations with Banach*. These pages contain carefully numbered questions concerning functional analysis that they discussed and deliberated upon, most likely in the University building at 4 St. Nicholas

---

[22]See biographical note B-1.
[23]See Biographical note B-2.

Street, between September and the end of December 1944. The questions were written into the notebook somewhat later, and they were based on earlier original notes from these sessions. I would like to quote these questions here to highlight some of Stefan Banach's interests at the time.

Copy of two pages from Andrzej Alexiewicz's university progress report with entries by Eustachy Żyliński , Hugo Steinhaus, Herman Auerbach, Stanisław Mazur and Stefan Banach.

1. A space X has a basis x_n. An abstract function

$$x(t) = \sum_{n=1}^{\infty} a_n(t)x_n.$$

is given. Under what assumptions

$$x'(t) = \sum_{n=1}^{\infty} a_n'(t)x_n \ ?$$

2. Are Sachs's theorems true in an abstract space (S)?

3. What about Tonelli's theorem on functions with bounded variation in the case of abstract functions?

4. Theory of lengths of curves for abstract functions.

5. Differential equations for abstract functions.

6. Definition of orthogonal abstract functions. The functions $x(t)$ and $y(t)$ are orthogonal if

$$\int \xi(x(t))\xi(y(t))dt = 0$$

for any $\xi \in \Xi$. Study orthogonal expansions of abstract functions.

7. Unification of a theory of abstract functions.

8. Theory of integrals of abstract functions over rings. Integration of products possible there.

21 September 1944

9. Fantapi's definition in the space of analytic functions. A closed set F is given. Z denotes the space of functions regular on a certain open set $G \supset F$. Then $z_n \to z_0$ means that $z_n(t) \to z_0(t)$ in some open set G_0, where $G \supset G_0 \supset F$.

10. Other definitions of convergence in the space of analytic functions.

   Z – the space of regular functions on the plane with possible exception of a finite (countable, 1st category) set.

   $z_n \to z_0$ means that for all sufficiently large n, $z_n(t)$ has the same singularities as $z_0(t)$, $z_n(t)$ converges almost uniformly to $z_0(t)$ in the complement of the set of singular points.

11. The same space as in 10, but with fixed singular points.

12. Under what assumptions is a space of type (Λ) of the second category? (separable)

Rozmowy z Banachem

(1) Przestrzeń X ma bazę : x_n.

Funkcje abstrakcyjna

$$x(t) = \sum_{n=1}^{\infty} a_n(t) x_n.$$

Przy jakich założeniach

$$x'(t) = \sum_{n=1}^{\infty} a'_n(t) x_n \qquad ?$$

(2) Czy twierdzenia Saksa są prawdziwe w abstrakcyjnej przestrzeni (S).

(3) Jak jest z twierdzeniem Tonelli'ego o f. o ogr. wahaniu dla funkcyj abstrakcyjnych

(4) Teoria długości krzywych dla f. abstr.

(5) Równania różniczkowe dla f. abstr.

Facsimile of the first page of manuscript by Andrzej Alexiewicz with the heading
Conversations with Banach.

13. Under what assumptions is it possible to prove that a function of the first Baire class additive in a space of type (Λ) is linear? (By a function of the first Baire class one can either understand a limit of continuous functions or define it in Borelian terms).

14. Define the integral for functions $x(t)$ (e.g., continuous) of a real variable with values in a space of type (Λ).

15. Abstract functions from $[0,1]$ to a space of type $(\mathcal{F})$. $x(t)$. It is likely that the following theorem is false: if $x'(t) = 0$, then $x(t) = \text{const}$.

A side annotation: "That is false!"

16. Study $(\mathcal{F})$-spaces, in which the theorem on linear functional extension is true.

14 December 1944

17. A 1-1 transformation from a disk into a disk (that is, increasing – so, in a sense, of bounded variation) is given. Suppose the field derivative exists (the generalised Jacobian). Can it be expressed in terms of partial (or approximative) derivatives?

18. Is it possible to approximate a 1-1 transformation from a disk to a disk by regular transformations (Lipschitzable transformations, analytic transformations)?

19. Is there a nontrivial theorem on passing to the limit in Denjoy integrals (i.e. not reducible to the Lebesgue integral)?

20. Find an elementary proof of the Hardy-Littlewood theorem for functions with bounded variation.

15 December 1944

21. The area of an abstract surface. Let the functions $x = x(u,v)$, $y = y(u,v)$, $z = z(u,v)$ be real.

Definition of bounded variation (two, different?)

(1) When each of the pairs (x,y), (y,z), (z,x) is of bounded variation, that is,

$$\int_{-\infty}^{\infty} u(v)dv < \infty$$

(2) For every sequence of increasing sets E_n

$$\sum |(x,y)E_n| < \infty.$$

Theorem: If a_{ik} is a nonsingular table and x, y, z are of bounded variation, then the functions $a_{ik}(x, y, z)$ are of bounded variation, too.

Definition. Abstract functions x, y, z are called of bounded variation, if for any $\xi, \eta, \zeta \in \Xi$ functions $\xi(x(u, v))$, $\eta(y(u, v))$, $\zeta(z(u, v))$ are of bounded variation.

Definitions of absolute continuity? Assuming high regularity it can be done as follows:

I take an orthogonal system x_n in X (a basis) and have

$$x = \sum a_n(u, v) x_n, \dots$$

and formally

$$\frac{\partial x}{\partial u} = \sum \frac{\partial a_n(u, v)}{\partial u} x_n, \dots$$

The area is to be equal to

$$\int \int \sqrt{\left[\frac{\partial(f_i, f_j)}{\partial(u_i, u_j)}\right]^2} \, du dv$$

$=$ using the Lagrange identity

$$= \int \int \sqrt{\left\|\frac{\partial x}{\partial u}\right\|^2 \left\|\frac{\partial x}{\partial v}\right\|^2 - \left(\frac{\partial x}{\partial u}\frac{\partial x}{\partial v}\right)^2} \, du dv$$

$$= \int \int \left\|\frac{\partial x}{\partial u}\right\| \left\|\frac{\partial x}{\partial v}\right\| \sin \gamma \, du dv$$

definitions

$$\cos \gamma = \frac{\int \int \frac{\partial x}{\partial u}\frac{\partial x}{\partial v} du dv}{\left\|\frac{\partial x}{\partial u}\right\| \left\|\frac{\partial x}{\partial v}\right\|}$$

22. If X, Y are of type $\mathcal{F}$, is it possible to introduce a reasonable concept of limit in $[X, Y]$?

23. Given a sequence ξ_n defined on a linear space $X_1 \in X$, $\xi_n(x) \to \xi_n(\alpha)$ in X_1. Can they be extended so that the extensions are convergent?

24. Is theorem 1 true for linear operations (M_γ^0)?

15 December 1944

25. Convergence in terms of relations: given a relation $(x\ R\ y)$ on X. $x_n \to x$ means that $\prod_x \sum_{N_x}$, i.e. $\left(\prod_{n \geq N_x} x_n R x_0\right) \to x R x_0$. Ordinary convergence corresponds to the relation $x R y \equiv |x - y| < 1$.

26. Measurable functions.

Def. 1: $\xi(x_1(t)), \xi(x_2(t))$ are independent for $\prod \xi \in \Xi$

Def. 2: $\xi(x_1(t)), \eta(x_2(t))$ are independent for $\prod \xi, \eta \in \Xi$

These are equivalent.

Is the following theorem true?

If x_n are independent $x_n(:) \in L^2$ (what L^2), $\int x_n dt$ are uniformly bounded (in what sense of $\int$) and $\sum a_n^2 < \infty$,, then the series $\sum a_n x_n$ is convergent presque perfect?

Notes from the last documented session, Friday, 29 December 1944, are as follows:

27. What are the theorems on passing to the limit in the integrals of Bochner, Pettis, Gelfand, etc.?

28. When is an absolutely continuous abstract function an integral?

29. The Riesz-Fischer theorem (strong?, weak?)

30. The integral equation

$$y(s) = f(s) + \lambda \int K(s,t)y(t)dt$$

can be studied if: (I) $y(t)$ is an abstract function and kernels are real, (II) $K(s,t)$ is abstract.

31. Partial differential equations for abstract functions: the Laplace theorem (strong and weak), the Poisson formula for the ball.

32. Integral equations in rings of type B (related to the integral there).

33. There exists a nontrivial example of ternary multiplication, which is not generated by binary multiplication (Banach). Can any finite set with ternary commutative multiplication be extended so that ternary multiplication is generated by a binary multiplication?

This was probably the last study session Professor Banach held with his youngest student, Dr Andrzej Alexiewicz. Next to some of the questions in the journal there are short annotations by my father that he made after the war.

And that was the end of their joint sessions. During the night of 2/3 January 1945, my father's mother Dr Zofia Link-Alexiewicz was arrested by the NKGB and put in prison at Łącki Street in Lvov. On 5 February, during a time of very cold weather, she was deported to the NKGB Gulag[24] (No. 0310) in Krasnodon. My mother, Julia (née Klonowska), shocked by this tragedy, gave premature birth on 8 January 1945 to a small and weak infant, my brother Tadeusz. In view of the arrest and deportation of my grandmother, my parents' only safe recourse was to abandon their house at Rewakowicz St. and leave their beloved Lvov to go west in a transport that included many of the staff of the Jan Kazimierz University.

My father and Professor Orlicz, his Ph.D. thesis advisor, left for Poznań in April, where, for over half a century (sic!), they continued the traditions of the Lvov School of Mathematics. After a short stay in Krakow my mother, together with her sons, joined my father. Unfortunately little Tadeusz did not survive the exodus and died in Poznań on 10 July 1945. Shortly thereafter we received very sad news of the demise of my grandmother Zofia in the Gulag in "the inhuman land" on 1 June 1945. In turn, the news of Stefan Banach's death in Lvov, on 31 August 1945, was a painful blow to all Polish mathematicians, already decimated as a result of the war, and was at the same time an irretrievable loss to mathematics.

In the preface to the *Introduction to the Theory of Real Functions* by Stefan Banach, there is the following statement [48]:

> *At the request of the editors of* Mathematical Monographs, *Professor Władysław Orlicz and Docent Andrzej Alexiewicz, former students of Banach, undertook to complete the missing sections of chapters whose fragments had survived. They knew the author's intentions from several conversations he had had with his colleagues and students about the book he planned to write (...)*
>
> *The missing parts written by Orlicz and Alexiewicz contain fragments relating to w-dimensional space (pp. 73–103), continuous functions (pp. 104–114 and 119–122), convergence of series of functions (pp. 127–130), Baire function (pp. 144–150) and continuous curves (pp. 155–161).*

During his entire life my father was fascinated by the genius of Stefan Banach. He used to stress that mathematics was indebted to Banach for

---

[24]Gulag – a network of forced labor camps in the USSR. Its inmates were criminals as well as persons deemed to be socially undesirable or politically suspect.

the three fundamental theorems of functional analysis. In the preface to his
book *Functional Analysis* he writes [47]:

*It is not possible to omit in a preface the role of the Polish School of Mathematics in
the development of functional analysis. Although Banach himself considered Vito
Volterra the creator of the theory of linear operations, and thus also of functional
analysis, it is Banach who should be considered its real creator, at least in its
mature form. This is not because he was the first to provide the definition of
a normed linear space, but rather because he was able to perceive the fundamental
and essential parts of the future theory and all of the basic inferences that follow
from it. Together with Steinhaus he founded the Lvov School of Mathematics,
which, with the participation of Schauder, Mazur and Orlicz, was responsible for
the prolific progress of mathematical analysis during the period between the two
wars. In his 1932 monograph, which to this day has not lost its topicality, Banach
blended into a unified whole the studies of his great predecessors: Hilbert, Riesz,
Fréchet, Hahn, to give the discipline a compact form. It included all of the basic
theorems discovered by him and his coworkers. Even today most ideas used in
functional analysis are just modifications of those of Banach.*

In his review of Roman Kałuża's book [19], in 1980, my father wrote,
among others:

*To this day not many people realise that the greatest Polish mathematician of all
time (the greatest after Copernicus according to the assessment of the anthropologist Czekanowski[25]) lived in Lvov during the twentieth century (...). I was in
contact with Banach during the occupation – his assessment of the political situations was always apt. At the beginning of 1945 Banach had no signs of cancer.*

During his interview with Nina Nowakowska, Father stated [73]:

*I saw Professor Banach for the last time in March 1945. It was said that he had
been invited to Moscow. It was rumoured that he was summoned by Stalin who
offered him the presidency of the Polish Soviet Republic (sic!). Of course, I take
no responsibility for these rumours. Very shortly after returning to Lvov he died in
August 1945 from lung cancer.*

My father maintained good relations with Stefan Banach's son, Stefan
Banach Jr[26], MD, a physician. Shortly after my father's death I found
a Christmas greetings card in the mail box that Stefan Banach Jr had sent
to him in December 1995. I cannot resist the temptation to quote a passage
from it:

I have a great favour to ask of you. Namely, I would timidly like to ask you – as the

---

[25]See biographical note B-6.
[26]See biographical note B-3.

*only and the youngest of my father's students – and as my friend, to write about
the way, the struggle, the result of his coming to his final achievement. BUT –
but... I would dream of it being a Christmas Eve story to be told over a glass of
vodka, the holy wafer and a marble-top table – a story spun for the semi-initiated,
or uninitiated who love mathematics – or a story consisting of just memories of
him. You are the only one who can create such a Christmas jewel. I know how
difficult it is, but I would have something to leave to my grandchildren. You bring
together all that is connected with him: the Łomnicki family, who took care of
him, and Lvov, and the Scottish Café. With great affection, Stefan.*

I believe that in the world beyond ours, the complete circle of Lvov
geniuses is sitting at a marble table deliberating and busily filling new pages
in the *Scottish Book*.

Poznań, 7 March 2007

Władysław Alexiewicz
(Translated by *Piotr Zarzycki*
with comments of *Wiktor Bartol*)

UNIWERSYTET JANA KAZIMIERZA
WE LWOWIE

SPIS WYKŁADÓW

W ROKU AKADEMICKIM 1939/40

LWÓW
WYDAWCA: UNIWERSYTET JANA KAZIMIERZA WE LWOWIE
TŁOCZONO W PIERWSZEJ ZWIĄZKOWEJ DRUKARNI WE LWOWIE, UL. LINDEGO I, 4
1 9 3 9

The facsimile of "Lecture Schedules for the Academic Year 1939/1949" at
The Jan Kazimierz University in Lvov (the title page)

68

Żatko Rudolf:

I. II. III. *Kurs niższy języka słowackiego*, 2 godz. piątek 14—16. (Sala XI).

I. II. III. *Kurs wyższy języka słowackiego*, 2 godz. piątek 16—18. (Tamże).

Lektorat języka francuskiego. (Nazwisko lektora będzie podane później).

I. II. III. *Kurs niższy ogólno-uniwersytecki języka francuskiego*, 2 godz. środa, piątek 11—12.

I. II. III. *Kurs wyższy ogólno-uniwersytecki języka francuskiego*, 2 godz. środa, piątek 12—13.

I. II. III. *Kurs niższy języka francuskiego dla romanistów*, 2 godz. wtorek, czwartek 12—13.

I. II. III. *Kurs wyższy języka francuskiego dla romanistów*, 2 godz. wtorek, czwartek 11—12.
Salę oznaczy się później.

Lektorat języka ormiańskiego. (Nazwisko lektora, oraz dzień i pora wykładów zostaną podane później).

V. WYDZIAŁ MATEMATYCZNO-PRZYRODNICZY.

Zapisy na ćwiczenia i seminaria wymagają uprzedniego zezwolenia profesora.
Bliższe wskazówki co do zapisów na wykłady i ćwiczenia podają ogłoszenia Zakładów.

Na tablicy ogłoszeń Wydziału w obu gmachach Uniwersytetu (ul. św. Mikołaja 4 i Marszałkowska 1) ogłoszone będą ewentualne dodatkowe wykłady, jakoteż uzupełnienia i zmiany, dotyczące wykładów i ćwiczeń, wymienionych w niniejszym programie.

Celem uzyskania po ukończeniu studiów uniwersyteckich stopnia magistra studenci Wydziału Matematyczno-Przyrodniczego mogą wybór wykładów i ćwiczeń stosować do obowiązujących w ciągu studiów egzaminów.

Dopuszczenie do niektórych ćwiczeń wymaga uprzedniego zdania przepisanych egzaminów. Dla niektórych przedmiotów zastrzega się kolejność egzaminów. Szczegółowe plany studiów i egzaminów magisterskich są zestawione w osobnej broszurze.

1. Logika.

Chwistek Leon dr prof z.:

I. II. III. *Podstawy logiki i metodologii*, w I. trym. 3 godz. -czwartek, piątek, sobota, 13—14. (Sala im. Kopernika), w II. i III. trym. 2 godz. piątek, sobota 13—14. (Tamże).

I.   *Wstęp do logiki formalnej*, 1 godz. środa 13—14. (Sala XII).

II. III.   *Logika formalna*, 2 godz. wtorek, czwartek 13—14. (Tamże).

I.   *Podstawy teorii klas*, 1 godz. wtorek 13—14. (Tamże).

The facsimile of "Lecture Schedules for the Academic Year 1939/1949" at
The Jan Kazimierz University in Lvov (page 68)

69

I. II. III. *Seminarium logiczne*, 2 godz. poniedzialek 18--20. (Zakład logiki).

I. II. III. *Proseminarium logiczne*, 2 godz. piątek 18 20. (Sala XII. i XV). (Przeznaczone dla kandydatów do egzaminu z Głównych zasad nauk filozoficznych).

I. II. III. *Ćwiczenia z logiki formalnej*, 2 godz. czwartek 18 20. (Sala XV).

2. Matematyka.

Żyliński Eustachy dr prof. z.:

I. II. III. *Analiza* (funkcje wielu zmiennych), 2 godz. piątek 11 13. (Sala I).

I. II. III. *Ćwiczenia do powyższego wykładu*, 2 godz. czwartek 11--13, (Tamże).

I. II. III. *Algebra wyższa*, 3 godz. poniedziałek 12 13, środa 11 13, (Tamże).

I. II. III. *Ćwiczenia do powyższego wykładu*, 2 godz. sobota 11 13. (Tamże).

I. II. III. *Seminarium matematyczne* (wyższe), 2 godz. wtorek 11 13. (Tamże).

I. II. III. *Ćwiczenia z geometrii analitycznej*, 2 godz. sobota 18—20. (Tamże).

Steinhaus Hugo dr prof. z.:

I. II. III. *Równania różniczkowe zwyczajne*, w I. trym. 4 godz. wtorek, środa, czwartek, piątek 11 12, w II. trym. 3 godz. środa, czwartek, piątek 11 12, w III. trym. 2 godz. czwartek, piątek 11 12. (Sala XII).

I. II. III. *Statyka graficzna*, 1 godz. poniedziałek 11--12. (Tamże).

II. III. *Nomografia*, w II. trym. 1 godz. wtorek 11 12, w III. trym. 2 godz. wtorek, środa 11 12. (Tamże).

I. II. III. *Seminarium z analizy*, 2 godz. wtorek 18 20. (Tamże).

I. II. III. *Ćwiczenia z metod graficznych*, wraz z doc. dr Auerbachem, 1 godz. sobota 11 12. (Tamże).

Banach Stefan dr prof. z.:

I. II. III. *Rachunek różniczkowy i całkowy*, 4 godz. poniedziałek, środa, 9—10, sobota 9 11. (Sala I).

I. II. III. *Teoria operacji*, 1 godz. poniedziałek 10 11. (Tamże).

I. II. III. *Balistyka*, 1 godz. środa 10--11. (Tamże).

The facsimile of "Lecture Schedules for the Academic Year 1939/1949" at The Jan Kazimierz University in Lvov (page 69)

70

L II. III. *Ćwiczenia z rachunku różniczkowego i całkowego*, 2 godz. poniedziałek 18—20. (Sala II).

I. II. III. *Seminarium*, 2 godz. czwartek 18—20. (Sala I).

Ruziewicz Stanisław dr doc. prof. em.:

I. II.   *Wyznaczniki i równania liniowe*, 2 godz. środa, piątek 19—20. (Sala I).

Schauder Paweł Juliusz dr doc.:

I. II. III. *Mechanika teoretyczna*, 3 godz. wtorek, czwartek, piątek 8—9. (Salę oznaczy się później).

I II. III. *Ćwiczenia z mechaniki teoretycznej*, I godz. piątek 10—11. (Sala I).

I. II. III. *Seminarium z analizy wyższej* (równania różniczkowe, cząstkowe, rachunek wariacyjny, topologia etc), 2 godz. Dnie, godziny i salę oznaczy się później.

Kaczmarz Stefan dr doc.:

I. II. III. *Matematyka dla przyrodników*, 3 godz. czwartek, piątek, sobota 8—9. (Sala XII).

I. II. III. *Ćwiczenia z matematyki dla przyrodników*, 2 godz. wtorek 18—20. (Sala II).

I. II.   *Zarys historii matematyki elementarnej*, 1 godz. środa 18—19. (Sala XII).

Auerbach Herman dr doc.:

I. II. III. *Teoria ciał wypukłych*, 1 godz. piątek 17—18. (Sala XV).

I. II. III. *Teoria potencjału*, 1 godz. środa 16—17. (Sala XII).

I. II. III. *Ćwiczenia do powyższego wykładu*, 1 godz. środa 17—18. (Tamże).

Mazur Stanisław dr doc.:

I. II. III. *Geometria różniczkowa*, 1 godz. wykładu, 1 godz. ćwiczeń, czwartek 18—19 (Sala XII), piątek 18—19. (Salę oznaczy się później).

I. II. III. *Seminarium z teorii metod sumowalności*, 2 godz. poniedziałek 18—20. (Sala XII).

3. Astronomia.

Rybka Eugeniusz dr prof. n.:

I. II. III. *Astronomia ogólna*, 4 godz. czwartek, piątek 16—18. (Sala wykładowa Zakładu geologicznego).

The facsimile of "Lecture Schedules for the Academic Year 1939/1949" at The Jan Kazimierz University in Lvov (page 70).

TRANSLATION: List of Lectures on Mathematics and Logic

List of lectures for the 1939/1940 academic year of the Jan Kazimierz University in Lvov:

V. FACULTY OF MATHEMATICS
AND NATURAL SCIENCE

Registration for classes and seminars is on the condition that one has the professor's permission.

Further instructions concerning registration for lectures and classes are announced by the various departments.

If necessary, the information about additional lectures, complementary studies or changes concerning classes and lectures listed in this programme will be announced on the faculty notice board in both of the University buildings (4 St. Nicholas Street and 1 Marszałkowska Street). The students of the Faculty of Mathematics and Natural Science may choose lectures and classes that are appropriate for the obligatory examination to be taken during their studies in order to graduate as Master of Science.

Admission to certain classes is contingent upon passing the requisite exams. For some subjects the proper sequence of such exams is required. Details concerning study plans and examinations for the Master of Science degree are provided in a separate brochure.

1. LOGIC

Chwistek Leon, Ph.D., Full Professor:

I.II.III. [a] Basics of logic and methodology. I. 3 hours per week on Thursdays, Fridays and Saturdays at 13:00–14:00 (in the Copernicus Lecture Room). II.III. 2 hours per week on Fridays and Saturdays at 13:00–14:00 (Copernicus Lecture Room).

I. Introduction to Formal Logic, one hour per week on Wednesdays at 13:00–14:00 (Lecture Room XXII).

II.III. Formal Logic, 2 hours per week on Tuesdays and Thursdays at 13:00–14:00 (Lecture Room XXII).

---

[a]Stands for 1st, 2nd and 3rd trimester.

I. Basics of Theory of Types, one hour per week on Tuesdays at 13:00–14:00 (Lecture Room XXII).

I.II.III. Seminar on Logic, 2 hours per week, on Mondays at 18:00–20:00 (Department of Logic)

I.II.III. Seminar on Logic, 2 hours per week, on Fridays at 18:00–20:00 (Lecture Room XXII and XV). (Intended for candidates for the examination on the main principles of philosophy).

I.II.III. Classes on Formal Logic, 2 hours per week on Thursdays at 18:00–20:00 (Lecture Room XV).

2. MATHEMATICS

Żyliński Eustachy Ph.D., Full Professor:

I.II.III. Analysis (functions of multiple variables), 2 hours per week on Fridays at 11:00–13:00 (Lecture Room I).

I.II.III. Classes for the Analysis lecture, 2 hours per week on Thursdays at 11:00–13:00 (Lecture Room I).

I.II.III. Advanced Algebra, 3 hours per week on Mondays at 11:00–13:00 (Lecture Room I)

I.II.III. Classes for the Advanced Algebra lecture, 2 hours per week on Saturdays at 11:00–13:00 (Lecture Room I).

I.II.III. Mathematics Seminar (advanced), 2 hours per week on Tuesdays at 11:00–13:00 (Lecture Room I).

I.II.III. Classes on Analytical Geometry, 2 hours per week on Saturdays at 18:00–20:00 (Lecture Room I).

Steinhaus Hugo, Ph.D., Full Professor:

I.II.III. Ordinary Differential Equations, in 1st trimester 4 hours per week on Tuesdays, Wednesdays, Thursdays and Fridays at 11:00–12:00, 2nd trimester 3 hours per week on Wednesdays, Thursdays and Fridays at 11:00–12:00, and in 3rd trimester 2 hours per week on Thursdays and Fridays at 11:00–12:00 (Lecture Room XII).

I.II.III. Graphic Statics, one hour per week, on Mondays at 11:00–12:00 (Lecture Room XII).

II.III. Nomography, in 2nd trimester one hour per week on Tuesdays at 11:00–12:00 (Lecture Room XII), in 3rd trimester two hours per week on Tuesdays, Wednesdays at 11:00–12:00 (Lecture Room XII).

I.II.III. Seminar on Analysis, 2 hours per week on Tuesdays at 18:00–20:00 (Lecture Room XII).

I.II.III. Classes on Graphical Methods, together with Assistant Professor Dr Auerbach, one hour per week on Saturdays at 11:00–12:00 (Lecture Room XII).

Banach Stefan, Ph.D., Full Professor:

I.II.III. Differential and Integral Calculus, 4 hours per week on Mondays, Wednesdays at 9:00–10:00, on Saturdays at 9:00–11:00 (Lecture Room I).

I.II.III. Theory of Operations, one hour per week on Mondays at 10:00–11:00 (Lecture Room I).

I.II.III. Ballistics, one hour per week on Wednesdays at 10:00–11:00 (Lecture Room I).

I.II.III. Classes on Differential and Integral Calculus, 2 hours per week on Mondays at 18:00–20:00 (Lecture Room II).

I.II.III. Seminar, 2 hours per week on Thursdays at 18:00–20:00 (Lecture Room I).

Ruziewicz Stanisław, Ph.D, Professor Emeritus.

I.II. Determinants and Linear Equations, 2 hours per week on Wednesdays, Fridays at 19:00–20:00 (Lecture Room I).

Schauder Paweł Juliusz, Ph.D., Assistant Professor:

I.II.III. Theoretical Mechanics, 3 hours per week on Tuesdays, Thursdays, Fridays at 8:00–9:00 (the lecture room will be announced later)

I.II.III. Classes on Theoretical Mechanics, one hour per week in Fridays at 10:00–11:00 (Lecture Room I).

I.II.III. Seminar on Advanced Analysis (differential equations, partial differential equations, calculus of variations, topology, etc.), 2 hours per week. (a timetable will be provided later)

Kaczmarz Stefan, Ph.D., Assistant Professor:

I.II.III. Mathematics for students of natural science, 3 hours per week on Thursdays, Fridays, Saturdays at 8:00–9:00 (Lecture Room XII).

I.II.III. Mathematics classes for students of Natural Science, 2 hours per week on Tuesdays, Fridays, Saturdays at 18:00–20:00 (Lecture Room II).

I.II. Basic Knowledge of the History of Elementary Mathematics, one hour per week on Wednesdays at 18:00–19:00 (Lecture Room XXII).

Auerbach Herman, Ph.D., Assistant Professor:

I.II.III. Theory of Convex Fields, one hour per week on Fridays at 17:00–18:00 (Lecture Room XV).

I.II.III. Theory of Potentials, one hour per week on Wednesdays at 16:00–17:00 (Lecture Room XIII).

I.II.III. Classes for the lecture on the Theory of Potentials, one hour per week on Wednesdays at 17:00–18:00 (Lecture Room XIII).

Mazur Stanisław, Ph.D., Assistant Professor:

I.II.III. Differential Geometry, one hour of lectures and one hour of class exercises on Thursdays at 18:00–19:00 (Lecture Room XII) and on Fridays at 18:00–19:00 (the lecture room will be announced later).

I.II.III. Seminar on the Theory of Summation Methods, two hours per week on Mondays at 18:00–20:00 (Lecture Room XII).

[...]

(Translated by *Anna Markiewicz*)

3.7   Wacław Szybalski about Stefan Banach

This interview with Professor Wacław Szybalski [27] was conducted by Dr John J. Greczek[28]

Q: *When and in what circumstances did you become acquainted with Stefan Banach?*

A: Already as a student in grammar school (high school or gimnazium-liceum) No. VIII in Lwów,[29] I would occasionally attend the lectures of renowned Lwów professors of mathematics, physics and chemistry, including lectures by Banach, from 1938 to 1939. As a chemistry student at the Lwów Polytechnic from 1939 to 1941, during the cruel Soviet occupation, I also attended these lectures, which were always delivered in Polish. Mathematics fascinated me, and I have to say that I was probably quite talented in the subject, at least in the opinion of my teachers and classmates. I was interested mainly in differential calculus and topology. In my house I had quite a large collection of mathematics textbooks, many of which I was able to successfully gather and protect after the bombings and fires during the fighting in September 1939, and June 1941. I also attended lectures by other leading Lwów mathematicians, such as, Antoni Łomnicki, Włodzimierz Stożek and Kazimierz Bartel [30]. Under Bartel, I passed examinations in descriptive geometry and perspective, and I felt that I was his favourite student. When I asked him once whom he considered to be the most outstanding Polish mathematician, he replied at once (perhaps partly in jest): "Bartel and Banach (Ba & Ba)", but added jokingly that the only reason he could match, and maybe even surpass, Banach is that as a prominent geometrician his brain was tri-dimensional "3D", whereas others had "flat" brains, and because he had twice held the office of Prime Minister of Poland! But I got to know Stefan Banach really well only later during the occupation of Lwów by the Germans from 1941 to 1944. Immediately after entering Lwów the Germans closed down the University and the Polytechnic from 1941 on, because "Poles do not deserve higher education". To avoid being arrested, deported (and worse), I started a full time job in the Weigl Institute, at 4 St. Nicholas Street, in the old Lwów University building.

---

[27]See biographical note B-19.

[28]See biographical note B-10.

[29]Professor Szybalski insisted on using the 600-year old name of the Polish city of *Lwów,* rather than the Russified-English transcription, *Lvov,* so as to honour Banach's preferences, and because this was the name known and used by Banach, in addition to the French *Leopol.*

[30]See Biographical note B-4.

I became head of a group breeding healthy lice (to be used for the production of typhus vaccine), and Professor Weigl decided that to this group of 20 to 30 people would be added mainly professors from the Lwów higher institutions of learning, and that I would actively look after them. I selected mainly the mathematicians, including Stefan Banach, because I thought I would learn a lot from them and benefit from being in their company and listening to their discussions every day for a few hours. Also, as a former Boy Scout and diehard Lwów patriot, I imagined I could somehow protect them from the dangers of war. The professors were in grave danger because the German SS, only days after they entered Lwów, murdered over 22 of them, often together with their entire families and houseguests.

Q: *How did Banach escape being executed on that night of 3/4 July 1941, together with the other professors? How did he, through chance (as you yourself have previously stated), escape with his life?*

A: That he was not taken that terrifying and terrible night had to be the result of a pure lottery of "life and death". The list of those selected for execution by the SS, without any pretense of a trial, must have been drawn up by the Germans and their Ukrainian collaborators before 1939, because it included professors who had died between 1939 and July 1941 (during the first Soviet occupation). Through some miracle Banach, and a number of other Lwów professors, were not on the list. The Germans were officious and systematic; they murdered only according to this list dating from 1939/40. In those days it was mainly chance that decreed whether someone lived or died. Many of us engaged in very risky undertakings. But at that time, when those who perished did so mainly because of bad luck (executions, war activities, mass homicides, etc.), there was probably only a small difference in the percentages of those who died, when one compares those who were risk takers with those who tried to avoid any risks.

Q: *What position did Stefan Banach have at the university at that time?*

A: During the first Soviet occupation (1939 to July 1941) he was Professor of Mathematics at the University, just like he had been before the war, and he lectured in Polish, mainly because among Lwów citizens practically no one was familiar with the Russian language. Banach was very respected by Soviet mathematicians and was chosen as a corresponding member of the Kiev Academy of Sciences. During the German occupation (1941 to 1944), when the Jan Kazimierz University (UJK) was closed down as a higher institution of learning, Professor Weigl (a colleague of Banach at UJK) provided him with shelter and assured his safety from the Germans by employing him as a feeder of healthy lice in his institute. During this period Banach was under my care (from 1941 through 1942), and later under my and Docent Stefania Skwarczyńska's joint care (until 1944). To avoid any risks, we tried to speak as little as possible about the fact Banach was working with us, so as not to "tempt the devil", because Banach was world famous and his wife was of Jewish extraction, which was a lure for the Germans and the "Volksdeutsch" (those locals who officially applied to be categorised by the Germans as being ethnic Germans). Banach's department at the "Old University", at 4 St. Nicholas Street, was housed in the same building as the Weigl Institute. In 1941, when the Weigl Institute took over most of that building for the production of the vaccine, I seem to recall that Banach retained his private office there. It was one of the rooms in Weigl's expanded institute, and he would often spend time there. However, that is no longer very clear in my memory.

Q: *Was he interested in politics?*
A: At that time of war everyone was interested in politics, and the fate of the world. However, listening to foreign radio stations was punishable by death. Despite that, my father and I (since I knew English well) always listened to the BBC, either in Weigl's office or at his home (he had some kind of German permit), or at my house. Transmissions in English and Italian (I knew both languages) were not being jammed by Germans as effectively as were those in the Polish language. The next day we would brief the "safe" Poles. Professor Banach would always ask me for details, in private, after feeding the lice. The noted Polish anthropologist Professor Jan Czekanowski would often come to our house at around 6 a.m. to get the latest world news. Professor Banach was not in such a great hurry to get the most recent news, but he was very worried about the fate of many Lvovians who were deported during 1939 to 1941 by the Soviets to gulags (forced labour camps) located throughout Russia from areas around Moscow to Siberia and Kazakhstan. Some 25,000 Polish army reserve officers were thus interred in such camps in Kozielsk, Putym, Ostaszków and Starobielsk. Those deported were men, some of whom he knew personally, who before the war had worked in civilian life as judges, teachers, professors, lawyers, physicians and in other professions. He was very happy when I told him that some had succeeded in joining Anders' Polish army that had formed in the Soviet Union after 1941, and later departed for Iran and farther destinations. Although we suspected the worst about the 25,000 captured by the Soviets when all letters from them stopped in 1940, Stefan was heartbroken when news arrived confirming that the Soviet NKGB had bestially murdered them all, in the forest of Katyń and in other places. There was no doubt among

us that these executions were the work of the Soviets in 1940 (as they finally admitted in 2002) while they were still allied with Nazi Germany. Banach then said, as I remember and try to paraphrase him: "This dastardly act of genocide by the Soviets is not very different from Nazi actions, with the exception that it is genocide, and that the German army doesn't murder officers who are prisoners of war". Banach and all of us were very depressed! Soviet and German atrocities are also discussed in my 1999 and 2003 articles about the Weigl Institute [34, 35].

Q: *What kind of person was he?*

A: Professor Banach truly loved mathematics with all his heart. He always told me that I should love it too because it is the most powerful and the most magnificent creation and expression of the human soul, and has been so since times immemorial. I was under his influence and remember these words (however, in Polish) particularly well, especially since he was always very pleasant and cordial towards me. Perhaps this unique relationship existed because I was "his" student, full of admiration for him as a mathematician, and, at the same time, I was his supervisor in the work with feeding the lice. He probably also liked me because almost every day I would relate to him all the latest "forbidden" radio news from all over the world. We also shared the same passion as other Lvovian inhabitants: a boundless love of Lwów, a love that in his case was, for instance, exemplified by his rejection of the very generous offer from the USA, as relayed through Professor John von Neumann. It was "too little", he once told us when feeding the lice, for which to abandon Lwów and his cherished group of Lvovian mathematicians. Perhaps it was this mutual love of Lwów that, at one time, made him suggest to me that we should address each other by the more familiar term "ty, and to drink a "Bruderschaft" ("brudzio" in Lvovian, a brotherhood drink) to that. I felt highly honoured because in those days students did not address professors in such a familiar way, unlike today, for instance, at American universities. It was very difficult for me to overcome tradition together with my feelings of great respect, to be able to address him that way, but Banach enjoyed such "shocking" behaviour! However, in his discussions and conversation he was usually very ironic. Often he was very cynical and pessimistic, and in that respect he differed a lot from my generation of optimists, who were a quarter of a century younger. But he liked jokes and lighthearted stories about interesting subjects. In our group of lice feeders there were two older and noted microbiologists, both Lwów University professors, Seweryn and Helena Krzemieniewski, who taught us a lot about bacteria. Stefan also liked the stories of Dr

Alexander Kosiba, a meteorologist who, over a number of years, had taken part in polar expeditions, where he said meat tasted best eaten raw, just as we now eat *sushi*. At that time, however, that seemed to us to be a story of quite exotic behaviour, and I saw from Stefan's expression that it was somewhat distasteful to him. But knowing him as I did, I suspect that despite that, he would have liked to try it – just out of curiosity and for the thrill of it.

Q: *Do you recall when Professor Banach spoke about his rejection of John von Neumann's offer?*

A: I heard that from the lips of Stefan Banach himself, when he spoke about it during a conversation at our table while feeding the lice in the Weigl Institute at 4 St. Nicholas Street, as I already mentioned. Any subject related to the love of Lwów was close to my heart and I remember, as though it were yesterday, when he said, with a tinge of irony: "I answered von Neumann that any such offer would always be too small for me to leave our dear Polish Lwów and all of you" (I saw he meant the Lvovian mathematicians because he turned to them when he said that, as we all sat at a table feeding lice). Thank you for this question because it refreshed my memory and I now recall that moment very well. But these recollections of von Neumann's offer came up several times in discussions in my lice-breeding department as we met there often, almost daily, for nearly three years. Stefan was noticeably "proud" of the answer he had given von Neumann, but I remember that at one time (1943/44) he asked: "Will von Neumann and other American mathematicians remember us now, and will they really help us somehow when we are being persecuted and murdered by the Germans, and when the Soviets still want in the future to seize our dear Polish Lwów?". I must admit that neither Banach, nor the inhabitants of Lwów, nor I, understood at that time why we should be worried about that, despite the fact that during the first occupation (1939–1941) the Soviets incorporated Lwów into their territories and deported some 20 percent of its population. The professors around the table held long discussions, while feeding the lice, on the subject of the future of Polish Lwów. Practically everybody was convinced that Polish Lwów would return to its pre-WWII glory, greatly assisted by the USA (with its millions of Polish-Americans). Banach was saying that the USA was honour-bound, as the WWII ally of Poland, to assure that would happen. Because the treacherous ally, the Soviet Union was, between 1939 and 1941, allied with Germany, supplying them with food and war materials and murdering, imprisoning and deporting large numbers of Poles, of which we were all aware, Banach argued: "How could the USA permit Lwów to be illegally taken away by the Soviet Union, a country which has committed all these barbarous acts of genocide against Poland". That was the thinking in Lwów just before the second Soviet occupation in 1944. However, already in the winter of 1943/44, Banach did not feel well and became somewhat pessimistic, while frequently underscoring that it was our sacred duty to always remember Lwów's tragedy during the Soviet and the German occupations, broadcast it "urbi et orbi", and to struggle efficiently and wisely for the future of Polish Lwów's destiny. It turned out that, unfortunately, Banach's pessimism was justified, and that as a result of the second Soviet occupation Lwów was ethnically "cleansed" by the Soviet administration. All of the pre-WWII population was forcibly deported, either to war-torn Western Poland or to Soviet gulags and wilderness areas of Siberia, while the Soviets requisitioned and appropriated their homes and all their property. An example was the confiscation of homes belonging to our family,[31] without any compensation, already now for 67 years. Similarly, many of those who, together with Banach, were lice feeders were expelled and lost their homes and all their possessions in Lwów. The victims of this brutal ethnic cleansing, assuming they survived, had to start their lives again from practically nothing.

Q: *Did his wife and son also work as lice feeders?*
A: I think his wife Łucja (the dear Lusia[32]), who purchased and started the *Scottish Book*, did not. Stefan loved her very much and worried about her constantly during the time of the *German hangmen* (as he called them). I remember that during 1941 she would bring treats for Stefan (as he fed the lice) and often for the rest of us in the lice-feeding room. But quite early on, in fear of persecution by the Germans, she left and went to Krakow (or its environs), for greater safety, because she was of non-Aryan descent. She is not on the list of those who worked in the Weigl Institute. His son Stefan is listed as one of the lice feeders. However, I do not remember him that well because he was not in my group. He also probably left early on to go to Krakow (or environs), also for greater safety in fear of the Germans, because of his mother's non-Aryan ethnicity. I heard from Dr John Greczek that in 1943, in Krakow, he became the godfather to a child born to the Greczek family.

---

[31]Houses at 2 St. Mark St. (where my brother and I were born), at 4 St. Mark St., 32 Zyblikiewicz St., also at 19 Długosz St., and others. The proofs of ownership of these houses have been retained and they are in our possession in Madison, WI, USA. (Author's note).

[32]Lusia – pet name for Łucja (Lucy).

Q: *Did he already know at that time that he was suffering from cancer?*
A: Probably at that time he did not realize that he was gravely ill with cancer. It's likely the full and more severe symptoms of the illness did not manifest themselves until somewhat later (Professor Weigl's Institute discontinued its work in Lwów in March 1944, whereas Banach's illness did not develop fully until January 1945). I had always advised him to stop smoking, telling him it was a killer habit. He was almost a chain-smoker. I often told him that he had a really bad cough and that was a bad sign. However, I thought he might be suffering from lung tuberculosis. He looked so sickly that I tried to persuade him that he should "look to me as an example" because I never touched a cigarette and that was why I felt healthy and strong. But I was never able to convince him by this argument. And poor Stefan looked so exhausted, and perhaps at times he was hungry and downcast. I have to admit that sometimes I hardly noticed him for days at a time, as he sat very quietly at our large table, while some others spoke in very loud voices. Another reason was that at that time I was attending many chemistry lectures at the Polytechnic and was at the Institute only during evening hours. (The Polytechnic had been renamed the *Technische Fachkurse*, however, it functioned practically in the same way as the pre-war Lwów Polytechnic – Politechnika Lwowska – considering the lecturers that were given, the use of the Polish language and its overall programmes.) Whenever I spoke with Stefan about his health he would always emphasize that he liked stress and that it helped him to work and create. He said not to worry about him because that was his nature. I naively believed him that stress was good for him because I, too, liked stress, and still do, and a little danger too. I remember that, at the time public exams were held, I was able to solve difficult differential equations at the blackboard, whereas I could not have succeeded if I had tried to do so on my own, in very quiet surroundings and without any stress. Because of his poor health and to help him, I cheated a little with the number of lice in his cage (I would put in 5 to 10 times fewer) whenever I saw that he seemed tired. I did not want him to lose too much blood. I considered it legitimate to cheat with the number of lice for the good of Polish mathematics and for the good of our beloved Lwów. It should, however, be emphasised that it was not the work with lice, but smoking, that was the cause of the cancer! (After all, several thousand of the intelligentsia rescued by Professor Weigl also worked as lice feeders, and three noted mathematicians among them lived to be 87 to 97 years old.) But now I know that, unfortunately, it would not have

helped even if he had stopped smoking in 1941, when I tried to persuade him to do so. In his genetic makeup he must have had harmful oncogenes that, in combination with the combustion products of tobacco, condemned him to a death that, in those times, could not have been prevented. That was already his sad fate probably at 30 to 40 years of age when he became a professor and a member of the Polish Academy of Arts and Sciences.

What a tragic loss that was for Lwów, for Poland and for the whole world of mathematics!!!

Q: *Were there any other mathematicians who worked in the lice breeding department under your supervision?*
A: Working in my group I remember were the following mathematicians (in addition to Banach): Feliks Barański (1915–2006), Bronisław Knaster (1893–1980) and Władysław Orlicz (1903–1990).

Q: *Did they utilize the time spent feeding lice in discussions of mathematics, or what other subjects did they speak about?*
A: Of course, they used the time to discuss various subjects including mathematics. Unfortunately, much of that has faded from my memory, but for me discussions of topology and set theory were the most interesting. On occasion, the mathematicians would agree on a certain time (since in general I did not require them to observe very specific hours for the feeding) for one of them to deliver a short colloquium, after which a general discussion would follow. But I would have to watch to make sure that, during the excitement of their discussions, the feeding did not exceed 45 minutes, because laboratory lice would lose their natural instinct to stop their consumption when already full, with ruinous consequences, because their intestines would begin to burst as a result of the excess blood in them. Alcohol consumption was not allowed when feeding the lice. The feeders would use alcohol together with the highly toxic mercuric chloride sublimate to disinfect their skins prior to attaching the lice cages to themselves so as to protect the lice from any infection. The lice had to be sterile, and only in the last stage were they infected by interannal injection with typhus bacteria, *Rickettsia prowazekii*.

In the group of professors seated at the table feeding lice, Banach was rather quiet and preferred to listen than to talk a lot. The "loudest" of the mathematicians was Professor Knaster, whose voice I always heard during nearly half of the feeding sessions. Similarly "loud" at our table was Mieczysław Kreutz, however, he was a psychologist and not a mathematician, and thus always held forth on various subjects. But frequently their conversations were about politics and they would recall and talk about the

continuing tragedies of the German occupation. We were all very greatly
concerned when Banach was arrested. I did not know why that happened,
but the rumours were that it was because of currency trading. At that time
that was quite common and everyone bought or sold hard (gold) and soft
(paper) dollars and other currencies. I hurried to see Weigl to ask for his
help. He already knew about the arrest and in his typical manner said:
"What has our Stefan done now? We shall go to rescue him anyway". (I remember well that he used the word "rescue".) Fortunately, this time Stefan
Banach was, indeed, relatively easily rescued from his predicament, and as
usual that was thanks to Weigl's courageous and well-conceived intervention. With Weigl's support we also tried to hide and save Poles of Jewish
extraction from persecution, and Banach also supported us strongly in this,
although we were all well aware that Poles accused of helping Jews were
immediately shot by the Gestapo or SS. However, our instructions from the
Polish underground home army AK "Żegota", our Boy Scout training, and
our moral principles, were for us stronger and more important than the
German terror and the fear of execution.

Professor Weigl exploited the Germans' immense fear of epidemic typhus.
The German army thought that Weigl's vaccine would be its deliverance
from Russian lice and typhus. The Germans were well aware that it was lice
that destroyed Napoleon's army, which had marched on Moscow. Ironically,
however, through its production and use, Weigl's vaccine helped the Poles
in the country and in the Ghettos more than it did the German armies.

Q: *Professor Szybalski, what do you think about moving Stefan Banach's
remains from Lwów to Krakow?*
A: Marshal Józef Piłsudski's[33] heart is buried in Vilnius in the Rosa Cemetery, and his body in the Wawel Castle in Krakow. The same should be
done with Professor Banach. People could then visit and honour him, and
pray, both in Krakow and in Lwów!

> *Dr John J. Greczek* spoke with
> *Professor Wacław Szybalski* in
> Madison, WI, USA, on 10 March 2007.
> (Translated by *John Greczek* and *Wacław Szybalski*)

---

[33]See biographical note B-15.

3.8 Tadeusz Riedl[34] about Stefan Banach

My father, Tadeusz Riedl, a doctor of law, and Stefan Banach became friends at the time of the German occupation. This was during the years 1941 to 1944. They would meet every week at the house of Michal Halaunbrenner, later a Professor who held the chair at the Department of Physics of the Krakow Polytechnic.

Already in the first few days of the second occupation by the Soviets, that is towards the end of July, 1944, my father suggested to Banach that he should come together with his family to stay in one of the apartments of our villa at 12 Dwiernicki Street. The apartment had previously been occupied by the Germans. Banach quickly accepted my father's proposal inasmuch as he was in a difficult situation with respect to accommodation. We note, in passing, that during the early years of the 1920s and 1930s he stayed together with his wife and son at the Professors' Residency at 11 Supinski Street (currently home to the Consulate General of the Republic of Poland), in 1933 for a short time at 22 St. Hyacinth Street, and from 1934 in comfortable accommodations at 23 Zyblikiewicz Street (tel. 204-85), in close proximity to the University. Two houses away (at 27 Zyblikiewicz Street) was where Stanislaw Ulam resided. Today these houses are differently numbered as 51 and 55, respectively. Following when their accommodations at Zyblikiewicz Street were first unlawfully occupied by strangers the Banachs decided to come to our villa. In August 1944 they moved into a 220 sq. meter apartment consisting of six rooms on the second floor of the villa. They were able to make use of the furniture there that the Germans had not had time to plunder. Banach had very good working conditions there. From the apartment he had a direct entrance through a long wooden walkway to the villa's large garden where he liked to spend time working in the midst of the greenery. He was also back at work in his old department at the newly reconvened university. During a period of several months my parents would meet quite frequently with Banach and his wife Lucja.

They met just as neighbours would in our first floor apartment. In addition, Banach liked to participate quite regularly in informal social gatherings that were hosted by my parents on Thursdays. These included a wider circle of my parents' friends and acquaintances. The gatherings, during which the current political situation was the main subject of conversation, were attended by Dr. Jan Kinel, Director of the Dzieduszycki Natural History

---

[34]See biographical note B-17.

Museum, who lived nearby, Alexander Krawczyński, former Director of the
Gebethner and Wolff Library in Paris (at 123 Boulevard Saint Germain)
who after the war directed the Gdansk-Wrzeszcz Library (at 66 Grunwald
Street), Professor Edward Sucharda, Chair of Organic Chemistry and Rector of the Lvov Polytechnic (1937-1939), Michal Halaunbrenner, already
mentioned above, who resided in a distant part of town and Dr. Paweł
Csala, Vice-President of the Chamber of Commerce in Lvov, Honorary Con-
sul of Finland and Papal Chamberlain.

It so happened that one afternoon a drunken Soviet officer invaded our
apartment accompanied by a private armed with a rifle. The officer, Sal-
nikov by name, had resided with us during the first Soviet occupation.
When he ordered the private to point the rifle at my father, and with my
mother standing in front of the rifle to protect my father, I (then 11 years
old) ran to the second floor to ask Professor Banach to help. Banach and
I then immediately ran downstairs together, at which the aggressors re-
treated.

During the summer of 1945 Banach's health began to deteriorate rapidly.
During those summer days I was an altar server at the church of St. Vincent
de Paul on Snopkowska Street and would see Lucja Banach there almost
every day attending morning Mass.

During the afternoon of the 31st of August Stefan Banach passed away
from cancer. His wife Lucja and my mother were present at his death.
He died in the large room with a balcony. During the next several days
much help was provided to Banach's widow by his colleagues and coworkers,
most of all by Professor Władysław Nikliborc. The day before the funeral
he came to us asking for a hammer and nails to be able to properly secure the
coffin lid. At that time my father was away making funeral arrangements
with the cemetery's administration. The scholar's funeral took place on the
4th of September. The funeral procession started from Dwiernicki Street
and progressed towards the Old Building of the Jan Kazimierz University
on St. Nicholas Street where the funeral service was held, and from there
to the Lyczakow Cemetery. Banach was buried there in the Riedl family
sepulcher.

During the autumn of 1969 I had occasion to personally observe that
the sepulcher was not sealed pointing to the possibility that it had been
penetrated by criminal elements. In Wroclaw I informed Professor Bronisław Knaster about this fact. His intervention with the Soviet Academy
of Sciences proved effective. The entrance to the sepulcher was sealed but
its desolation was not stopped. In addition to the marble side slabs of the

The Professors' House at 11 Supinski Street.

House at 22 St. Jacek Street.

House at 23 Zyblikiewicza Street.

The Riedl family house
at 12 Dwiernicki Street.

sepulcher plundered earlier, the marble cross of the head stone has been knocked down. Now it can only be seen in a photograph taken earlier.

More recently, in 2002, the Dean of the Lvov University Mathematics Department showed me in the departmental offices the original of Banach's handwritten communication to the Soviet authorities concerning an increase in remuneration.

Gdańsk – Sopot, November 2008   *Professor Tadeusz Riedl*
                                         (Translated by *John Greczek*)

Chapter 4

Stefan Banach in the Light of Archives

Stanisław Domoradzki[1] (Rzeszów)

Zofia Pawlikowska-Brożek[2] (Krakow)

Mikhailo Zarichny[3] (Lvov)

Many years of quest for materials related to the Lvov School of Mathematics resulted in a collection of information found in the District Archive in Lvov, the Archive of the State University in Lvov and in various other archives. In this chapter we exhibit the effect of research related to the person of Stefan Banach. Personal dossiers of other mathematicians making part of the Lvov School of Mathematics had also been taken into consideration. The information they contain sheds more light on the figure of the creator of the School.

The archives of Lvov provide many documents that reveal the personality of not only an eminent scientist, which Stefan Banach was, but also that of a man trying to cope with usual living problems, searching for funds needed to maintain his family - wife and son. Taking into account the liberal way of life of this great scientist, who attached real significance only to mathematics, such problems must have raised barriers difficult to overcome.

Several letters dated between 1922 and 1939 and preserved in the District Archive of Lvov under pressmark (F.26, op.5, spr.58 Teka Stefan Banach)

---

[1]See biographical note B-7
[2]See biographical note B-14
[3]See biographical note B-24

expose a dramatic correspondence between the bursary of the Jan Kazimierz University (JKU) in Lvov and Stefan Banach's creditors claiming repayment of loans given to Banach against his salaries.

1. Letter of Stefan Banach, Prof. Extraordinary, to the Academic Senate of the JKU asking for an advance pay of his two-month salaries to be used to move to a new flat.
   Dated September, 30, 1922.

2. Letter of the Ministry of Religious Creeds and Public Education to the Rector's Office of the JKU, to prof. dr Stefan Banach, informing of the reimbursement of travel costs to Warsaw. Also a draft of a hand-written information for the Dean's Office at the Faculty of Philosophy.
   Dated December 30, 1922.

3. Letter of March, 12, 1923 to S. Banach. The Senate of the JKU refused to pay an advance on the salary.

4. Letter from the Lvov Polytechnic to the JKU Rector's Office asking for the return of money unduly paid to Stefan Banach.
   Dated April 14, 1924.

In this sequence of letters there is one more optimistic:

5. On April 27, 1926, the Dean's Office of the Faculty of Maths. and Nat. Sci. sends an application for naming prof. dr S. Banach Full Professor. The Academic Senate accepts the motion at its meeting of May 10, 1926, and informs about it on June 11, 1926.

Not a minor factor of S. Banach's financial problems was the prolonged illness of his wife Łucja, confirmed by several medical certificates submitted to the Rector's Office.

6. Certificate on the illness of Łucja Banach, professor's wife, recommending long treatment in a health-resort, dated May 18, 1926 . Similar certificates were submitted on November 5, 1926, June 24, 1927, February 7, 1929.

7. Two letters from the Lvov Polytechnic to the JKU, dated October 22, 1926, and March 1927, about taking wages corresponding to hours contracted by Lvov Polytechnic into account in the calculation of due tax.

8. Two letters (January 26, 1928 and January 28, 1928) informing of Banach's dispensation from juryman's duties.

9. S. Banach's letter of September 27, 1930 to the Rector, asking for an advance on the salary (equivalent to 3 salaries) for medical treatment. Answer positive (September 27, 1930).

Several letters were concerned with the issue of the 2500 Polish zlotys (zl) grant that the Ministry of Religious Creeds and Public Education (MRCPE) paid to prof. S. Banach in November 1930 upon his request of February 18, 1930 to support research. The grant contained the condition that a report on the results of Banach's research would be presented to the Ministry before June 1, 1931.

10. Letters from the MRCPE to S. Banach via Rector's Office, dated February 19, 1932 and May 19, 1933, reminding Banach of the research report that should have reached the Ministry on June 1, 1931 at the latest. Lack of report could result in a demand to repay the grant. The letters were transmitted to the addressee by the Dean's Office.

11. Letter of the Ministry of Religious Creeds and Public Education (MRCPE) to the JKU Rector's Office, consenting to pay S. Banach due wages for hours contracted for general mechanics, provided the JKU had disposable funds.
Dated May 24, 1932.

12. Hand-written letter from the JKU Bursary to the JKU Rector's Office in reply to a letter about Banach's debt towards the JKU and manner of its repayment in instalments.
Dated June 3, 1933.

The next institution to demand repayment of a debt was the Town Communal Savings Bank (TCSB) in Lvov. S. Banach committed himself to repay his loan by monthly instalments of 200 zl to be deduced from his salary.

13. Letter from the TCSB to the JKU Rector's Office claiming 200 zl out of each S. Banach's monthly salary as repayment of the contracted debt. Dated August 28, 1933.

14. Letter from the JKU Rector's Office to the executive Officer of the City Magistrate Court concerning the claims of the Association of Fiscal Officials, by which we learn that S. Banach's monthly salary amounted to 1,040 zl, out of which 200 zl were deduced for the TCSB (until repayment of 6,433 zl).
Dated September 20, 1934.

15. A certificate issued by the JKU secretary's Office, stating that S. Banach is full professor at the JKU. Certificate to be used to obtain school fee reduction for his son Stefan.

16. Notification from the MRCPE informing that the Ministry had applied to the Ministry of Treasure for a reduced-price passport for S. Banach on his trip to Oslo.
    Dated June 30, 1936.

17. S. Banach's cession of September 21, 1937, valid till repayment of the 4,000 zl debt with 8% interest to the TCSB.

18. Letter from the JKU Bursary to S. Banach, dated January 1, 1938. A refundable loan of 500 zl had been granted until April 1, 1939. S. Banach's hand-written consent with the same date.

The facsimile of the cession on behalf of his wife Łucja. Document from the archival collection of the Institute of Mathematics of the Polish Academy of Sciences reproduced by kind permission of Professor Zbigniew Ciesielski

> **TRANSLATION: Stefan Banach's cession of fees**
>
> I hereby cede all the income flowing from my book titled Theoretical Mechanics to my wife and authorize her to receive the fees due for the above-mentioned book.
>
> Lvov, on July 9, 1936   Stefan Banach

And then another dramatic question turns up. The Ministry of Religious Creeds and Public Education granted professor Banach a loan equivalent to six monthly salaries, to be returned to the University. In order to secure repayment of the loan in case of S. Banach's demise, both him and his wife Łucja make statements. S. Banach's statement is not sufficient, it is required that some source of money be indicated. For that purpose S. Banach predestines money expected from the funeral fund of the Union of Academic Professors. However, only those who regularly pay due fees are entitled to such money.

19. Łucja Banach's declaration, addressed to the JKU Rector's Office, declaring repayment of the loan granted by the MRCPE in case of her husband's demise.
    Signed on October 4, 1938.

20. S. Banach's declaration on "ceding his death benefit in case of demise" to secure the six-month salary advanced granted by the MRCPE. Signed on October 4, 1938. The loan was to be repaid to the University.

21. Letter to the Union of Academic Professors in Lvov, informing of prof. S. Banach's cession of the amount of 1500 zl from the Funeral Fund of the Union "due to him by way of assurance" to secure the six-month salary loan granted to him.
    Dated October 5, 1938.

22. Information of the Union of Academic Professors addressed to the JKU Rector's Office and stating that the above mentioned security of loan repayment in case of S. Banach's demise is acceptable, provided due fees are deduced from his wages.
    Dated October 17, 1938.

23. Letter from the MRCPE of April 27, 1939, reminding S. Banach of the submission of a report on his stay at the International Congress of Mathematicians in Oslo in July 1936. To S. Banach's knowledge via Dean's Office.

Moreover, in the folder we find the following documents on the acquisition of academic degrees and the title of professor, as well as documents on Banach's teaching, research and organisational activities.

24. Letter of the JKU Faculty of Philosophy to the JKU Academic Senate, dated April 25, 1922. The Faculty Council had unanimously voted to grant S. Banach, docent (assistant professor) at the JKU, the right to lecture on mathematics.

25. MRCPE to the Faculty of Philosophy of the JKU on June 10, 1922. The Ministry cannot validate dr Banach's habilitation for the degree of Docent, since the lecturing language of his printed habilitation thesis not being Polish, as required by article 53 of the Academic Schools Act.

26. Letter of the JKU Senate to the MRCPE, dated June 12, 1922. The JKU Academic Senate on its session of June 10 voted to propose a motion to the MRCPE to allow S. Banach to lecture in French, French being the publication language of his habilitation thesis.

27. Manuscript letter of the Senate to the MRCPE. On its session of June 17, 1922, the Academic Senate accepted the motion to appoint S. Banach Professor Extraordinary in mathematics, presented by the Faculty Council.

28. Copy of a letter of the MRCPE to Mr dr Stefan Banach, docent at the JKU in Lvov, dated August 2, 1922. The Head of the Polish State appointed you Professor Extraordinary in mathematics at the Faculty of Philosophy of the Jan Kazimierz University in Lvov, to come into force on July 22, 1922 (bad quality of the writing).

29. The text of dr Stefan Banach's oath as professor of the JKU, September 18, 1922.

ROTA PRZYSIĘGI.

- Przysięgam Panu Bogu Wszechmogącemu, że na poruczonym mi stanowisku nauczyciela będę wiernie służyć i przyczyniać się będę w tym zakresie działania ze wszystkich sił do ugruntowania wolności, niepodległości i potęgi Rzeczypospolitej Polskiej, której zawsze wiernie służyć będę; wszystkich obywateli kraju w równem mając zachowaniu, przepisów prawa strzec będę pilnie, obowiązki mego urzędu spełniać gorliwie i sumiennie, polecenia moich przełożonych wykonywać dokładnie, a tajemnicy urzędowej dochowam.

Tak mi Panie Boże dopomóż"

Przysięgę służbową złożyłem dnia 17 września 1922 r. co stwierdzam własnoręcznym podpisem.

Dr Stefan Banach
Prof. Uniwersytetu Jana Kazimierza we Lwowie

Przysięgę odebrałem.

The facsimile of Stefan Banach's oath of office. Document from the Archive of the Lvov University, kindly supplied by Professor Mikhailo Zarichny

---

TRANSLATION: Text of Stefan Banach's oath of office

I swear to God Almighty that while executing my teacher's office I will contribute with all my force to the strengthening of freedom, independence and power of the Polish Republic, which I will always serve faithfully.

Holding all the citizens of my country in equal esteem, I will diligently preserve the stipulations of law, earnestly and conscientiously perform the duties of my office, accurately carry out instructions from my superiors and keep official secrets.

So help me God.

I confirm by my personal signature that I took the oath of office on September 18, 1922.

Dr. Stefan Banach Prof. of the Jan Kazimierz University in Lvov.

cm

I have sworn (Stefan Banach) in.

S. Narajewski

Rector

---

30. Letter of the University of Warsaw to the MRCPE, dated December 2, 1922. The Council of the Faculty of Philosophy (on its session of October 31, 1922) and the Senate of the UW (on its session of November 29, 1922) resolved to invite dr Stefan Banach, professor of the JKU, to give lectures in mathematics in the second trimester of the academic year 1922/23, the teaching load consisting of 5 hours of lectures and 2 hours of exercise classes.

31. In a letter of December 30, 1922, the MRCPE informs the JKU Rector's Office that "his activities at the University of Warsaw could only be remunerated by paying his travel expenses and daily allowances".

32. By its decree of February 17, 1925, the MRCPE informs S. Banach that on January 24, 1925 the President of the Polish Republic had conferred the title of Full Professor at the Faculty of Mathematics and Natural Sciences of the JKU on him.

33. The Dean's Office of the Faculty of Mathematics and Science informs prof. S. Banach of the above.

Ministerstwo W.R.i O.P.

    Warszawa,   Do Pana

   26 listopada   7   Dra Stefana B a n a c h a

IVS?/13663/27.   profesora nadzwyczajnego

                            Uniwersytetu Jana Kazimierza

                               we Lwowie.

           PAN PREZYDENT RZECZYPOSPOLITEJ mianował Pana Profeosra postanowieniem z dnia 17 listopada 1927 r.profesorem zwyczajnym matematyki na Wydziale matematyczno-przy rodniczym Uniwersytetu Jana Kazimierza we Lwowie.

           Zawiadamiam Pana Profesora o powyższej nominacji z tem, że dotychczasowy wymiar obowiązków Pańskich pozostaje nadal bez zmiany.

           Rektor Uniwersytetu Jana Kazimierza we Lwowie otrzymuje równocześnie upoważnienie do asygnowania Panu Profesorowi uposażenia służbowego, przywiązanego do zwyczajnej katedry w myśl Ustawy z dnia 9 października 1923 r./Dz.U.Rzp.P. Nr.116 poz.924/ wraz z dodatkiem za kierownictwo seminarjum od dnia 1 grudnia 1927r.

                          M i n i s t e r

          Wyznań Religijnych i Oświecenia Publicznego

                     /-/ Dr.Dobrucki

The facsimile of Stefan Banach's nomination as a full professor. Document from the Archive of the Lvov University, kindly supplied by Professor Mikhailo Zarichny

---

TRANSLATION: Nomination as a full professor

Ministry of R. C. and P. E.
Warsaw,
November 26,(192)7

> To Mr
> Dr Stefan Banach
> extraordinary professor
> Jan Kazimierz University
> in Lvov

By his decision of November 17, 1927, the President of the Polish Republic nominated you, Mr. Professor, as full professor in mathematics at the Faculty of Mathematics and Physics of the Jan

I hereby inform you, Mr Professor, of this nomination, providing that the duties you have been fulfilling till now remain unchanged.

The Rector of the Jan Kazimierz University in Lvov receives thereupon the authorization to assign to you, Mr Professor, the official salary associated with an ordinary Chair as stipulated in the Act of November 9, 1923 (Dz.U.Rzp.P. Nr.116 poz.924)[a] together with a supplement for heading a seminar, valid since December 1, 1927.

> Minister of Religious Creeds
> and Public Education
> (-) Dr. Dobrucki

---

[a]Journal of Official Acts of the Polish Republic, No.116, item 924

On the same card: the Faculty informs the MRCPE of the advance of the amount equivalent to 3 monthly salaries granted to S. Banach, presently in Paris on a research leave. Attached a medical certificate of January, 30, 1925.

On the same card: In a letter of February 26, 1925, the Academic Senate seconds the application for a three-month salary advance.

34. On August 11, 1925 the MRCPE informs that it cannot give course to the appointment of S. Banach for Full Professor, the 4th Chair of Mathematics being classified as Extraordinary.

35. On November 26, 1927 the MRCPE informs Prof. S. Banach that

by his decision of November 17, 1927 the President appointed him to the position of Full Professor in Mathematics at the Faculty of Mathematics and Natural Sciences of the JKU.

36. Letter to the Rector's Office of October 12, 1928: Prof. S. Banach and W. Stożek notify of the start of lectures and exercise classes in General Mechanics.

37. Letter to the JKU Senate of September 30, 1930. The Council of the Faculty of Mathematics and Natural Sciences had charged S. Banach with the lecture and exercise classes in General Mechanics. Banach signed acceptance of the charge.

38. Manuscript of a mathematical article with no date nor signature (9 loose pages).

39. Letter of November 24, 1939 with the inscription: Jan Kazimierz University in Lvov, St. Nicholas Str. 4, Mathematical Institute. The letter confirms that Menachem Wojdysławski had been conferred the degree of Master in Mathematics at the University of Warsaw in June of the present year. Signed by dr Stefan Banach, Professor at the University in Lvov.

From Stefan Banach's personal dossier in the Archive of the I. Franko State University in Lvov we mention the following documents:

1. Stefan Banach's employee's book (Trudovaya knizhka), issued on November 1, 1940 (with erroneous birth date).

2. Stefan Banach's personal questionnaire with a hand-written annotation by the Head of Human Resources stating that due to the demise of Stiepan Stiepanovich Banach, prof. dr of Mathematical and Physical Sciences, Head of the Chair of Mathematical Analysis, his name should be deleted from the list of University professors, to come into force on September 3, 1945. On the first page of the questionnaire Banach declared Polish nationality, wrote that he was not a Party member, that he had never travelled abroad, that he had been councillor in the Lvov Town Council since 1940, that his knowledge of foreign languages is limited to a poor knowledge of German and good knowledge of French, that among the languages of the Soviet Union he spoke poor Russian and good Ukrainian, that he suffered no repression following participation in the October Revolution, that he had served in no army, that in the period between June 1941 and July 1944 he worked as lice feeder at the Antityphoid Institute in Lvov, that he

was assistant at the Lvov Polytechnic in the years 1920-22, Professor at the University 1922-1939, Professor of the Lvov State University 1939-1945 and Head of the Chair of Mechanics at the Polytechnical Institute in Lvov 1944-1945.

3. Letter of November 13, 1944, to the Rector of the JKU, requesting to be dispensed of Dean's duties at the Faculty of Physics and Mathematics, the reason being intensive research work, which makes administrative duties hard to comply with. Hand-written Rector's annotation informing of dispensation from Dean's duties on November 15, 1944.

4. Stefan Banach's curriculum vitae in Ukrainian. Most probably written by Miron Zarycki, signed by S. Banach.

TRANSLATION: Stefan Banach's curriculum vitae:

Banach Stefan, father's name: Stefan, born March 30, 1892, in Krakow, Pole. Secondary-school certificate awarded by the IV Gimnazjum in Krakow in 1910. Higher education at the Lvov Polytechnical Institute in 1910-1914 and at the Lvov University in 1920-1922.
PhD in mathematics at the Lvov University 1920. Habilitation at the Lvov University, Faculty of Mathematics 1922.
Assistant in mathematics at the Lvov Polytechnical Institute 1920-1922.
Professor in mathematics at the Lvov State (!) University 1922-1939.
Professor and Head of the Chair of Mathematical Analysis at the Ivan Franko State University in Lvov 1939-1945.
During the nazi occupation worked as lice feeder at the Antityphoid Institute in Lvov.
Member of The Academy of Science in Krakow since 1924.
Prize of the Town of Lvov for research (7500 zl) in 1930.
Prize of the Krakow Academy of Science for research (20,000 zl) 1939.
Councillor in the City Council of Lvov since 1940.
Doctorate in physico-mathematical sciences and professorship approved by the All-Union Committee for Higher Education, March 9, 1941.
Dean of the Faculty of Physics and Mathematics at the Lvov State University in the years 1939-1944.

Lvov, May 16, 1945
Dvernicki Boulevard 12 app. 4
S.S. Banach

The facsimile of Stefan Banach's curriculum vitae (in Ukrainian) Most probably written by Miron Zarycki, signed by S. Banach.

5. Extract from an order of the Lvov State University Rector prof. Biliakiewicz (no. 86 of November 30, 1944) approving the staff of the Chair: professors and lecturers for the academic year 1944/1945 and the Head of the Chair prof. Stefan Banach.

6. Minutes of the Attestation Commission of the All-Union Committee for Higher Education of March 8, 1941, stating that Stefan Banach had been approved for the position of professor at the Chair of Mathematics and his scientific doctor's degree in physico-mathematical sciences at the Lvov State University confirmed.

7. Extract from an order of the Lvov State University Rector (no. 80 of November 24, 1944) confirming the recognition of prof. Stefan Banach's work at the University since August 1, 1944, after the liberation of Lvov from nazi occupation by the Red Army.

8. Certificate of August 3, 1944, stating that the Dean of the Faculty of Mathematics and Physics at the Lvov State University dr Stefan Banach resides in Lvov, at Dvernicki street 12 app. 4.

9. Stefan Banach's request to the Rector of the Lvov State University, prof. Biliakiewicz, of September 22, 1944. Prof. Banach asks for a budget for the organization of the 25th anniversary of the Ukrainian Academy of Sciences. Enclosed is a request for a 1000 rubel loan and a 1000 rubel advance on the nearest salary.

10. Another personal questionnaire.

11. Letter of May 27, 1941, bearing the seal of the Ivan Franko State University. The letter characterizes Szperling Mavrikiy Genselevich, assistant at the Chair of Mathematical Analysis. Written in Ukrainian, signed in Cyrillic: Dean of the Faculty of Mathematics and Physics S. Banach.

The Lvov District Archive also hosts several items related to the Jan Kazimierz University and the Lvov Polytechnic that in one way or another relate to Stefan Banach.

F. 27, op. 4 spr. 346. Personal dossier of Kazimierz Kuratowski. Lvov Polytechnic No. 2755/31.

1. Letter written by JKU mathematics professors to the Lvov Polytechnic Rector's Office concerning candidates for the extraordinary Chair

of Mathematics at the General Faculty of the Lvov Polytechnic, recommending K. Kuratowski (dated April, 9, 1926). Signed by Stefan Banach together with E. Żyliński, H. Steinhaus, S. Ruziewicz.

2. Letter of the Lvov Polytechnic Rector's Office to the Ministry of Religious Creeds and Public Education presenting K. Kuratowski for the nomination to the position of Professor Extraordinary in mathematics at the Lvov Polytechnic. Dated February 18, 1927.

   On p. 2 Banach is mentioned among those who replied to the offer of taking over the 3rd Chair of Mathematics after Włodzimierz Stożek.

3. Report on prof. dr Kazimierz Kuratowski's academic research and activities since his nomination as Professor Extraordinary at the General Faculty of the Lvov Polytechnic, dated May 22, 1931.

   On pp. 3, 4 Banach is mentioned as co-author of the paper "Sur généralisation du problème de la mesure" in *Fundamenta Mathematicae*, 13.

   On p. 88 the same appears on the list of K. Kuratowski's papers.

F.26, op. 5, spr. 1723. Jan Kazimierz University. Wacław Sierpiński dossier.

1. Letter from the Council of the Faculty of Mathematics and Physics of the JKU University to the Ministry of Religious Creeds and Public Education concerning the 2nd Chair of Mathematics headed by Stanisław Ruziewicz. Dated September 11, 1933. Mention on Stefan Banach being nominated as professor.

   Letter signed by the Dean Stefan Banach.

F.26, op. 5, spr. 1818.

1. Letter to the JKU Rector's Office on the teaching charge commissioned to dr Włodzimierz Stożek, dated September 16, 1933. Signed by the Dean Stefan Banach.

F. 26, op. 51, spr. 813. Stefan Kaczmarz dossier.

1. Report on the Faculty Council session at the JKU Faculty of Mathematics and Physics, May 18, 1929. S. Banach presents the motion to admit S. Kaczmarz to the habilitation process.

2. Minutes of the Mathematical Commission with Stefan Banach, June 5, 1929. Discussion of the academic achievements of S. Kaczmarz and on the admission of his paper "On the convergence and summability of orthogonal expansions" for his habilitation.

3. Report on the Faculty Council session at the JKU Faculty of Mathematics and Physics, June 7, 1929. S. Banach presents the motion to admit S. Kaczmarz to further stages of the habilitation process.

4. Report on dr S. Kaczmarz's habilitation examination, June 7, 1929. S. Banach posed the following questions:

    1. The present state of research on convergence and summability of orthogonal series.
    2. Non-Euclidean geometry.

5. Report on the Faculty Council session at the JKU Faculty of Mathematics and Physics, June 12, 1929. After S. Kaczmarz's habilitation lecture presented to the Faculty Council, S. Banach moves that *veniam legendi*[4] in the area of mathematics be granted to the lecturer.

6. Letter to the MRCPE of October 29, 1929, concerning S. Kaczmarz's habilitation. S. Banach presented the case.

F. 26, op.5, spr. 2093, 2094. J. P. Schauder's personal dossier.

1. Report on J. P. Schauder's habilitation on May 25, 1927. Reported by S. Banach.

2. Report from the session of the Commission for dr W. Nikliborc's habilitation, May 24, 1927. S. Banach present.

3. Report on the habilitation examination of J. P. Schauder on May 25, 1927. After hearing favourable opinions of prof. Banach (Steinhaus, Ruziewicz, Ernst and Lori), *veniam legendi* was granted. Prof. Banach asked: What are the basic problems of elliptic equations?

4. Report on J. P. Schauder's habilitation lecture, May 28, 1927. S. Banach present.

---

[4]the right to lecture to students

5. Letter of the JKU Faculty of Mathematics and Physics to the MRCPE concerning the habilitation and *veniam legendi* of J.P. Schauder. S. Banach mentioned twice (as Commission member present and as the person reporting the issue to the Faculty Council).

6. *Currenda* concerning J. P. Schauder's nomination as assistant at the Chair of Mathematics, October 10, 1933. S. Banach's signature.

F. 26, op. 4, spr. 668. M. Eidelheit's dossier.

1. Report on Eidelheit's PhD thesis, April 22, 1938. Reported by S. Banach. Also signed by H. Steinhaus.

2. Evaluation of M. Eidelheit's Master's thesis (summability theory) of May 31, 1933. S. Banach affirms that the paper had been written at his seminar. Signature of the annotation dated May 8, 1933.

3. S. Banach's affirmation that M. Eidelheit had written his PhD thesis in his Institute. Dated March 3, 1938.

4. In his curriculum vitae of March 3, 1938, M. E. states that he "works at the seminars of prof. Banach and doc. Mazur".

5. In M. E.'s PhD thesis presented to the Commission, which S. Banach was member of, on March 23, 1938 (examination on March 24, 1938) S. Banach is mentioned 5 times in references and once in the bibliography.

F. 27, op. 5, spr. 15978. S. Ulam's dossier.

1. Ulam's inscription card. Lvov Polytechnic, 1929/30. Third year of Ulam's studies. S. Banach inscribed as lecturer in Theoretical Mechanics.

Due to an initiative of prof. dr Zbigniew Ciesielski the Mathematical Archive in Sopot, affiliated by the Institute of Mathematics of the Polish Academy of Sciences, has been collecting documents on mathematicians and mathematics in Poland for many years. Traces of Stefan Banach can also be found there. These are photographs, that had already been published: the First Congress of Mathematicians from Slavonic Countries, Warsaw 1929, the second Assembly of Polish Mathematicians in Wilno, 1931 (both in [61], pp. 69 and 71). Assembly of the representatives of Mathematical Circles, Lvov 1930 (K. Kuratowski, S. Banach, E. Szpilrajn Marczewski, J. Schauder

can be seen on the picture, among others) (published in [21], p. 194), the first Assembly of Polish Mathematicians in Lvov, 1927.
There are also the following photographs:

(ZF.102) Banach with his son Stefan. An excursion of the Physico-Mathematical Circle in Lvov, 1931.

(ZF.7) International Congress of Mathematicians in Oslo, in 1936. A group of Polish mathematicians: S. Banach, B. Knaster, K. Zarankiewicz, K. Kuratowski.

(ZF.778) A group of mathematicians with W. Stożek and S. Banach.

The manuscript collection includes:

1. S. Banach's curriculum vitae written by A. Pełczyński for *Encyclopedia Britannica*.

2. S. Banach's curriculum vitae written by Z. Ciesielski on the occasion of Banach's commemorative year in 1992.

3. Typescript of S. Banach's paper *O mierze w ciałach niezależnych* (*On measures in independent fields*), Lvov, autumn 1940 (7 pp.).

4. Letter of Stefan Banach Junior to Zofia Pawlikowska-Brożek about the author's father Stefan Banach and the *Scottish Book*: l ist of authors of problems inscribed in the book. Dated April 26, 1989.

5. Typescript of Z. Pawlikowska-Brożek's paper *Stefan Banach w świetle wspomnień* (*Stefan Banach in the light of reminiscences*), with Stefan Banach junior's remarks on the margins.

6. Two xerocopies of certificates concerning Kazimierz Szałajko, signed by S. Banach.

7. Photocopies of the correspondence between S. Banach and Stanisław Ulam in 1937 and 1938.

8. Interview with Z. Semadeni on the 30th anniversary of S. Banach's decease ("Kurier Polski", 1975).

9. Biography of S. Banach by H. Steinhaus ("Nauka Polska", 1960).

(Translated by *Wiktor Bartol*)

Chapter 5

Banach's Opus Scientificus

Julian Musielak[1] (Poznań)

5.1 Predecessors

Already in the 19th century eminent mathematicians, such as N. Abel, J. Liouville, C. Neumann and H. Poincaré took interest in integral equations, i.e, equations where the unknown function f occurs in the integrand, as in the example below:

$$f(x) = \lambda \int_a^b K(x, y) f(y) dy + g(x). \tag{1}$$

The paper "Sur une classe d'équations fonctionnelles" (On a class of functional equations) published by Ivar Fredholm in 1903 was particularly significant. Fredholm reduced the problem of solving (1) to the solution of a system of linear algebraic equations. The equation (1) was given the name of *Fredholm linear integral equation of the second kind*. Decisive, however, were the papers of the German mathematician David Hilbert, published in the years 1904–1910 under the common title of "Grundzüge einer allgemeinen Theorie dcr linearen Integralgleichungen" (The Foundations of a General Theory of Linear Integral Equations). The basic assumption underlying Hilbert's results was that of the square of the function f being integrable. The set of such functions, called *Hilbert function space* or L^2 space, is related to the set of sequences (a_n) of their Fourier coefficients, called *Hilbert sequence space* or l^2 space. Both functions and sequences are considered to be

---

[1]See biographical note B-13

"points" of infinitely dimensional vector spaces. Such an interpretation has
since become the cornerstone of a new approach to functions and sequences,
now seen as geometric objects. Frigyes Riesz, a Hungarian mathematician,
referred to Hilbert's work in the years 1907–1918, when he published six
papers in which he generalised and developed Hilbert's results. A French
mathematician, Maurice Fréchet, in 1906, and a German mathematician,
Felix Hausdorff, in 1914, introduced the notion of a *metric*, understood as
an axiomatically defined *distance* $d(x, y)$ between points x, y in a space that
would then be called a *metric space*. In particular, such were the spaces
introduced by Hilbert and Riesz.

5.2   Banach Space

In 1922, Stefan Banach, who was then a young mathematician in Lvov,
published his Ph.D. thesis "Sur les opérations dans les ensembles abstraits
et leur application aux équations intégrales" (On Operations in Abstract
Sets and Their Application to Integral Equations) in the third volume of
Fundamenta Mathematicae. In the paper, which was, in fact, an impressive
entrée into world mathematics, Banach introduced the notion of a space that
was later termed *Banach space*. Let X be a real or complex vector space.
The elements of X will be called points. Assume that to each point $x \in X$
a nonnegative number $\|x\|$ is assigned so that the following conditions are
satisfied:

1° $\|x\| = 0$ if and only if $x = 0$,

2° $\|x + y\| \leq \|x\| + \|y\|$,

3° $\|cx\| = |c|\,\|x\|$ for every $x, y \in X$ and any number c (real or complex).

Then $\|x\|$ is said to be the *norm* of the point x and the ordered pair
$(X, \|\ \|)$ is called a *normed vector space*. The term "norm" is intended to
replace "length of a vector". When X is either the space of real numbers
or the space of complex numbers, the norm of x is taken to be the absolute
value of x: $\|x\| = |x|$. In a normed vector space the distance between two
points x and y is defined by $d(x, y) = \|x - y\|$. Given a metric space X
with distance d, we can define the notion of *convergence* for a sequence (x_n)
of its points by assuming that the sequence converges to a point $x \in X$
if $d(x_n, x) \to 0$ for $n \to \infty$. A sequence (x_n) is a *Cauchy sequence* if
$d(x_m, x_n) \to 0$ for $m, n \to \infty$. Every convergent sequence is a Cauchy

sequence. A space X is said to be *complete*, if every Cauchy sequence is convergent to a point in X. The notion of convergence in a metric space X with distance d can be expressed in terms of balls in the space. A *ball* $B(x_0, r)$ with centre $x_0 \in X$ and radius $r > 0$ is the set of all the points $x \in X$ that are at distance less than or equal to r from x_0, that is, when $d(x_0, x) \leq r$. A sequence (x_n) of points in X converges to a point $x_0 \in X$ if for every $r > 0$ the ball $B(x_0, r)$ contains all the elements of the sequence (x_n) except for a finite number of them. All the above notions can clearly be applied to a normed vector space $(X, \| \ \|)$ with distance $d(x, y) = \|x - y\|$. When $(X, \| \ \|)$ is complete under this definition of distance, the space is called a *Banach space*.

The definitions are very simple, which might lead one to think that little can be proved about notions thus introduced. It turns out that this is not so. In fact, these uncomplicated notions can be used as the basis for building a vast theory, a theory with multiple and important applications. That is what made Banach's theory so successful, and in this sense Banach can be considered the founder of functional analysis.

5.3 What is Functional Analysis about?

Functional analysis is the analysis of *operators* from a space X into a space Y. When Y is the space of real or complex numbers, an operator from X into Y is called a *functional*, which accounts for the name of the entire domain. An operator (functional) T from a vector space X into a vector space Y is *linear*, if $T(x_1 + x_2) = T(x_1) + T(x_2)$ and $T(cx) = cT(x)$ for all $x_1, x_2, x \in X$ and any number c. If X and Y are normed vector spaces and the linear operator T is continuous, i.e., when $\|x_n - x\| \to 0$ implies $\|T(x_n) - T(x)\| \to 0$ for $n \to \infty$, then T is a *continuous linear operator* (*functional*). Many mathematical objects are indeed linear operators or functionals, like the limit of a sequence or function, the sum of a series, the derivative and the integral. This explains why functional analysis is widely used in mathematical analysis, in the theory of orthogonal expansions, in the domain of integral or differential equations, and in many other areas of mathematics. Through these theories the usefulness of functional analysis extends to problems of modern physics and its applications.

Banach's main work, the book *Theory of Operations. Vol. I: Linear Operations* [3], is about such operators and functionals. It first appeared in 1931 published by Wydawnictwa Kasy im. Mianowskiego, and then in

1932, in an extended version *Théorie des opérations linéaires,* as the first volume of the series *Monografie Matematyczne* (Mathematical Monographs) financially supported by the Fund for National Culture.

For the next 25 years the book was the main source of worldwide inspiration and of citations for several generations of mathematicians working in functional analysis. This was due not only to its basic contents, but also to the *Remarks* that closed the book. The *Remarks* extended over 15 pages and commented upon open problems. The book often referred to the work of previous or contemporary authors, among whom a particular place was reserved for Frigyes Riesz. Polish mathematicians were abundantly quoted, too, with Stanisław Mazur, with whom Banach had written many research papers, most frequently. The other names quoted were H. Auerbach, K. Borsuk, S. Kaczmarz, K. Kuratowski, F. Leja, S. Mazurkiewicz, O. Nikodym, W. Orlicz, S. Saks, J. Schauder, H. Steinhaus, L. Sternbach, E. Szpilrajn (E. Marczewski),) S. Ulam, Z. Zalcwasser and A. Zygmund.

In 1958, two American mathematicians, Nelson Dunford and Jacob T. Schwartz. published *Linear Operators. Part I: General Theory* [13]. The book replaced Banach's book as a source of citations. In the second chapter the authors discuss three fundamental principles of linear analysis. All three are Banach's theorems, which reveals Banach's leading role in the development of functional analysis. Let us consider the partly simplified formulations of the principles. The first is the *uniform boundedness principle.* It states the following: *Let (T_n) be a sequence of continuous linear operators from a Banach space $(X, \| \ \|_1)$ into a normed vector space $(Y, \| \ \|_2)$ such that for each $x \in X$ the sequence $(\|T_n(x)\|_2)$ is bounded, i.e., for each $x \in X$ there is a number $M(x) > 0$ such that $\|T_n(x)\|_2 \leq M(x)$ for $n = 1, 2, \ldots$. Then this boundedness is uniform in every ball $B(0, r)$, i.e., for every $r > 0$ there is a number $M_r > 0$ such that for all $x \in B(0, r)$ and $n = 1, 2, \ldots$ the inequality $\|T_n(x)\|_2 \leq M_r$ holds true.*

The point is that the number M_r only depends on $B(0, r)$. A reader unaccustomed to mathematical texts will encounter serious difficulties when reading similar theorems. The difficulty lies in the repeated use of quantifiers: the general quantifier (*for all*) and the existential quantifier (*there exists*). The order in which the quantifiers are written is important. Such texts may require several readings and often the reader is required to complete the gaps in the text by himself. Banach proves the uniform boundedness principle by the so-called generic method, to which we will return further on. The principle finds numerous applications in mathematics, being particularly useful in mathematical analysis.

The second principle is the *open mapping principle*: *If T is a continuous linear operator from a Banach space $(X, \| \ \|)_1$ onto the entire Banach space $(Y, \| \ \|_2)$, then the image $T(G)$ of an arbitrary open set G in $(X, \| \ \|)_1$ under T is an open set in $(Y, \| \ \|_2)$.* The implications of the principle include the inverse operator theorem that states the following: *if T is a one-to-one map of $(X, \| \ \|)_1$ onto $(Y, \| \ \|_2)$, then the inverse operator T^{-1} from Y to X is also linear and continuous.*

Finally, the third principle is the Hahn-Banach theorem on linear functional extension. *Let X be a real vector space and let p be a real-valued function defined on X and such that $p(x + y) \leq p(x) + p(y)$ and $p(cx) = cp(x)$ for all $x, y \in X$ and $c \geq 0$. Moreover, let f_0 be a real linear functional on a subspace X_0 of the space X such that $f_0(x) \leq p(x)$ for all $x \in X_0$. Then there is a real linear functional f on X such that $f(x) = f_0(x)$ for all $x \in X_0$ and $f(x) \leq p(x)$ for all $x \in X$.*

This theorem, apparently purely theoretical, has found extensive applications to specific problems. Proved by Hahn for a Banach space X, it has been generalised by Banach for the case of an arbitrary vector space X. In fact, the generalisation to complex Banach spaces only came in 1938 and was due to H.F. Bohnenblust and A. Sobczyk.

Let us now take a look at one of the examples illustrating an application of the general form of the Hahn-Banach theorem. The example belongs to measure theory. A correct definition of a measure on the real line $\mathcal{R}$ was given by a French mathematician, Camille Jordan, in the 19th century. The measure of a set $A \in \mathcal{R}$ was defined so that

1° The measure of the union of finitely many pairwise disjoint measurable sets is equal to the sum of their measures.

2° The measure of an interval is its length.

3° A translation of a set along the line preserves its measure.

A function with property **1°** is said to be *finitely additive*. It turns out that many important sets, such as the set of all rational numbers in a given interval, have no measure in the sense of Jordan. The notion of measure on $\mathcal{R}$ was extended by the French mathematician Henri Lebesgue in the beginning of 19th century. Lebesgue's measure satisfies condition **1°** for countable unions of sets; such a measure is said to be *countably additive*. (Let's note that Lebesgue was awarded the title of honorary doctor at the Jan Kazimierz University in Lvov.) However, in 1905 the Italian mathematician Giuseppe Vitali showed that there still are sets that are not measurable in the sense of Lebesgue. The problem appealed to Banach. Using the method of extending linear functionals he proved the existence of a finitely additive measure on $\mathcal{R}$ that satisfies conditions $\mathbf{1}^o - 3^o$ and, moreover, every subset of $\mathcal{R}$ is measurable in the sense of this measure. The measure was actually a generalisation of that of Jordan. It is now called *universal measure*. However, the universal measure is not effective, which means that no explicit construction is known. To prove its existence the axiom of choice is applied.

5.4   Methods of Functional Analysis

One of the characteristic features of Banach and his school is the use of set-theoretical methods, mainly the category method. This is one of the ways of discerning "small" and "big" sets. For example, any finite set A of natural numbers is "small" when compared with the set of all the natural numbers in terms of the number of elements, i.e., in the sense of power. Similarly, the set $\mathcal{Q}$ of all the rational numbers is "small", in the sense of power, within the set $\mathcal{R}$ of all the real numbers. Indeed, $\mathcal{Q}$ is countable (all its elements can be ordered in an infinite sequence), whereas the set $\mathcal{R}$ is uncountable. On the other hand, the set of all the irrational numbers is "big" in $\mathcal{R}$, because it is the complement of a "small" set $\mathcal{Q}$. Another way of differentiating "small" and "big" sets is to compare their measures. In this sense a "small" set is a set of measure 0, while a set is "big" if it is the complement of a set of measure 0. This method of qualifying sets as "small" or "big" is important, e.g., in probability theory. A "small" set is an almost impossible event, i.e., an event with probability 0, and a "big" set is an almost certain event, i.e., an event with probability 1.

Let X be a metric space. The category method departs from *nowhere dense sets*, i.e., sets $A \subseteq X$ that are not dense in any ball in the space X. A union of the most countable number of such sets is a *set of the first category in X*. The French mathematician René Baire proved that *a complete metric space is never a set of the first category*. Hence the idea of taking sets of the first category in a metric space to be "small" sets and to classify their complements, known as *residual sets*, as "big" sets in the category sense. In particular, it follows from Baire's theorem that a residual set in a complete metric space must be non-empty. This fact is the core of existence proofs for objects with assumed properties: it suffices to show that the set of such objects is residual in a metric space. By consistently applying the distinction between "small" and "big" sets it can be proved that sets of very irregular functions can be "big". This is how Banach proved that the set of all continuous functions not differentiable over a set of positive measure is residual in the space $C(a, b)$ of all the functions continuous on the closed interval (a, b). Examples of such functions had already been known in the 19th century, though at that time they were seen as pathological. It was the application of the category method that showed that precisely the set of those "pathological" continuous functions without a derivative is "big", whereas continuous functions with a derivative except for a zero-measure set form a "small" set in the sense of category in the space $C(a, b)$. The method, called the *generic method*, proved to be very effective in various applications including, among others, in the theory of differential equations.

About half of Banach's papers attacked problems related to the classical roots of functional analysis. These were mostly papers on measure and integral theory and the theory of real functions, but also on Fourier series and orthogonal expansions. Fourier series was the topic of Banach's first paper "Sur la convergence en moyenne de séries de Fourier" (On the mean convergence of Fourier series) written jointly with Hugo Steinhaus. It appeared in the *Bulletin International de l'Académie de Sciences de Cracovie* in 1919. What was characteristic of these works was the application of methods very modern for that time because of the use of set theory and topology. Banach's results often exposed paradoxical properties of mathematical objects. Let us mention just one of them, the so-called *paradoxical decomposition of the sphere*. It appeared in the paper "Sur la décomposition des ensembles de points en parties respectivement congruentes" (On the decomposition of a set of points into correspondingly congruent parts) written with the Polish logician Alfred Tarski and published in *Fundamenta Mathematicae* **6**, 1924. Here is a concise presentation of the paradoxical result of this paper.

Let's call two sets A and B on the sphere $\mathcal{S}$ in $\mathcal{R}^3$ *congruent*, if there is a one-to-one mapping from A onto B such that the distance between any two points in A is equal to the distance in B between their images under the mapping. A set A is *equivalent* to the set B, if A and B can be decomposed into pairwise disjoint subsets $A_1, A_2, \ldots, A_n$ and $B_1, B_2, \ldots, B_n$, respectively, so that for each $k = 1, 2, \ldots, n$ the sets A_k and B_k are congruent. The Banach-Tarski theorem states that *a sphere $\mathcal{S}$ in $\mathcal{R}^3$ can be decomposed into a union of two disjoint sets A and B such that the set A is equivalent to the entire sphere $\mathcal{S}$ and the set B is equivalent to the entire sphere $\mathcal{S}$. In other words, by congruent transformations two spheres, each of the size of $\mathcal{S}$, can be obtained.*

The paradox is slightly attenuated by the fact that the parts of the decomposition are non-measurable, which means that the decomposition process cannot be implemented in practice.

Stefan Banach's research results quoted above are only a sample of his broad and deep work. What remains uncommented here includes, among others, operators conjugate to the given ones, the theorem on the weak compactness of a ball in a reflexive Banach space, the Banach-Mazur theorem on the universality of the space of continuous functions in the class of separable spaces, or the widely applicable fixpoint theorem for contracting mappings.

In 1941, the Russian mathematician I.M. Gelfand restructured the vector space X into a ring, where addition of elements of X and scalar multiplication were complemented by multiplication of elements. Objects so obtained were called *Banach algebras*. After Banach's death such algebras, just as other topics derived from Banach's work, were intensely investigated by mathematicians in Warsaw, where one of the most eminent disciples of Banach, Stanisław Mazur, had moved to.

Among Banach's successors was also Władysław Orlicz, the founder of the school of functional analysis in Poznań. Banach's ideas were brought to Wrocław by Hugo Steinhaus, who had once discovered Banach's great talents.

In the opinion of the writer, Stefan Banach is the most outstanding personality in the history of Polish mathematics.

(Translated by *Wiktor Bartol*)

Chapter 6

Stefan Banach and Lvov Mathematical School[1]

Krzysztof Ciesielski[2] and Zdzisław Pogoda[3] (Krakow)

Up to the end of the 19th century Poland was not noted for mathematics. The mathematical results obtained by Jan Śniadecki, Jan Brożek, Jan Kochański and some others were not enough to make Polish mathematics famous throughout the world. Note that in the 19th century, when mathematics in the world developed enormously, in times of Carl F. Gauss, Augustin L. Cauchy and Bernhard Riemann, Poland did not exist as an independent country. Poland had for two centuries been divided among Germany, Russia and Austria. Only in the area under Austria (which included Krakow and Lvov) the Poles had some opportunities of scientific research. Nevertheless, up to the First World War the best Polish scientists, like Maria Skłodowska-Curie, obtained their results mainly abroad. Some mathematicians, like Józef Hoene-Wroński and Stanisław Zaremba also worked abroad. Nevertheless, their advanced results did not make Polish mathematics in the end of the 19th century famous enough.

Everything changed after the First World War. Poland became a world mathematical power. In 1900 Zaremba moved to Krakow and created there a mathematical center. Immediately after the war some Polish mathe-

---

[1]This article was published in the monthly "*Wiedza i Życie*" (No. 8/1994, pp. 38–43); the English translation (slightly modified) is reproduced here with the permission of the authors and the publishers.

[2]See biographical note B-5.

[3]See biographical note B-16.

maticians formed the Warsaw Mathematical School. Their research were connected mainly with topology, a branch of mathematics which began to flourish at that time. The names of Polish mathematicians were widely known throughout the world. However, the greatest role in the fame of Polish mathematics was due to the Lvov Mathematical School and their members, among them, above all, Stefan Banach.

Hugo Steinhaus used to say that the discovery of Banach was his greatest mathematical discovery. This is a sentence of a particular importance, as Steinhaus was one of the greatest Polish mathematicians, the author of many outstanding results, one of the creators of the Polish Mathematical School. How was Banach "discovered" by Steinhaus?

In 1916, Steinhaus, by then a well-known mathematician, was taking a walk. Suddenly he heard the words "Lebesgue integral". Today this is one of the basic terms in mathematical analysis, but at the time it was a recent discovery known almost exclusively to specialists. Steinhaus was intrigued. He approached the two young people discussing mathematics – they turned out to be Stefan Banach and Otto Nikodym (later a well-known mathematician) – and joined their conversation. At one point he told them about a problem he had been working on for some time. Great was his surprise when next day Banach brought him the solution.

Stefan Banach was born out of wedlock in Krakow in 1892. His mother was Katarzyna Banach and his father was Stefan Greczek. He was brought up by the owner of a laundry, to whose care he was entrusted from birth. After completing school, Banach decided to study engineering in Lvov. He liked mathematics but decided that very little could be added to such a developed subject. Study at the Technical University did not appeal to him; he definitely preferred far-reaching generalizations to the problems he encountered there. He had to tutor in order to support himself. Small wonder that it took him four years to earn his so-called half-diploma (which required completion of two years of course work). At the outbreak of the First World War Banach returned to Krakow and enriched his mathematical knowledge by independent study. In mathematics, he was self-taught. He read a great deal and sporadically attended lectures at the Jagiellonian University. He also engaged in many discussions with his friends Witold Wilkosz and Otto Nikodym.

Steinhaus realized that Banach had a superb mathematical talent. Due to his intercession, Banach, who had not earned any degree, was appointed to an assistantship at the Lvov Technical University.

In 1920 Banach was granted the doctoral degree by the Jan Kazimierz

University at Lvov. Banach did not complete any course of study. Soon thereafter he was appointed professor. The story of the curious way Banach obtained his doctoral degree was told by Andrzej Turowicz, a priest and a Benedictine friar, who graduated in mathematics from the Jagiellonian University in 1928 and lectured at the Lvov Technical University before the Second World War. When he started working at the university, Banach had to his credit many important results and kept on making new mathematical discoveries all the time. When told that it was time for him to present a doctoral dissertation, Banach replied that he would do so as soon as he discovered a result better than the ones he had found so far. Finally the university authorities lost patience. Somebody wrote down Banach's remarks on some problems and these was accepted as a splendid doctoral dissertation. But an exam was also required. One day Banach was accosted in the corridor by a colleague and asked to go to the dean's office, because "somebody came and wants to know some mathematical details, and you will certainly be able to answer his questions". Banach willingly answered the questions not realizing that he was being examined by a commission that had come to Lvov for this purpose. Such a procedure would probably be impossible today.

Those who knew Banach claimed that he attached little significance to nonmathematical matters. He talked and thought mathematics all the time. He was always full of new ideas. Only a small part of his ideas and results was written down. This was because he thought it more interesting and important to do research than to write up his findings. It was said that in order to make sure that posterity would get all of his results it would have been necessary for him to be followed by three secretaries who would take down all he said.

Banach was very pleasant and friendly. He wasn't conceited, he didn't make an impression of being a great man. Although, as Turowicz said, one would guess that he knew what to think about himself.

An important role in shaping the atmosphere the Lvov mathematics worked in was played by their get-togethers in the *Scottish Café* on Academic Street, near the university. A great many of them, including Banach, spent long hours at the café eating, drinking, and posing and solving mathematical problems. They had the habit of writing solutions on marble table-tops. In this way many a theorem was lost forever. Finally, Banach's wife bought a notebook in which the mathematical habitués of the café recorded their problems. The notebook called the *Scottish Book* remained in the café and was brought by a waiter at the request of mathematical patrons.

Sometimes the person who posed a problem offered an award for its solution. Some of the rewards were unusual. Thus Stanisław Mazur offered a live goose for the solution of one of his problems. This was in 1936. A "mere" 36 years later the problem was solved by the then 28-year-old Swedish mathematician Per Enflö, who later came to Warsaw and received the prize from Mazur.

Some of the café sessions lasted many hours. In fact, one of them lasted 17 hours and yielded an interesting result that was wiped off the table-top by a conscientious waiter. There are those who claim that this was far from being the longest session, and that on one occasion two mathematicians got so involved in a discussion that they stayed in the café for 40 hours!

Many anecdotes, legends, and tales are associated with the café sessions. Once Stanisław Mazur presented a problem, and Herman Auerbach started to thinking it over. After some minutes Mazur, wanting to make a puzzle more interesting, added that he offered a bottle of wine as a reward. After a while, Auerbach said: "Oh, I give up. Wine does not agree with me".

Another story involves Henri Lebesgue, who arrived in Lvov in 1938 for the award of an honorary doctorate by the university. Lebesgue gave two lectures and, of course, was invited to the *Scottish Café*. A waiter gave Lebesgue the menu. Lebesgue, who did't know Polish, studied the menu for a while, gave it back and said: "I eat only dishes which are well defined".

The frequent café visits reflected certain aspects of Banach's personality and character. When he wasn't busy lecturing he could almost certainly be found in the *Scottish Café*. Its noise and airlessness seemed to suit him perfectly. There he could talk endlessly about mathematics, solve problems, and pose new ones. As a rule, after a long mathematical sessions at the Café, he would arrive the next day with sketches of the solutions of most of the posed problems.

Banach was surely the greatest mathematician in Lvov group, but there were also other excellent scientists.

The "discoverer" of Banach, Hugo Steinhaus (1887–1972) was an exceptional person. He was remarkably many-sided; he obtained significant results in many different areas of mathematics. A significant part of his scientific work involves practical, sometimes very surprising, applications of mathematics. He had an excellent ability to grasp applied problems in a mathematical way. During the war, he surprisingly precisely estimated Germany's losses. He read the obituaries in German newspapers, which said "the second son, the third son..." Using statistics and information about the number of families with two sons, three sons etc. he managed to guess the approximate losses of the German army. He had very original ideas and knew a lot. He was a man of great culture and deep knowledge of literature. His aphorisms, remarks, and thoughts are famous to this day. Here are a few that are (unfortunately, most of them, including the best, are not translatable):

"It is easy to remove God from his place in the universe. But such good positions don't remain vacant for long".

"Strip-tease should be strictly forbidden. This is the only way of keeping this beautiful and useful custom alive."

"It is easy to go from the house of reality to the forest of mathematics, but only few know how to go back."

Once, when somebody was decorated with a medal, Steinhaus said: *"Now I know what to do in order to be awarded a medal. Nothing, but for a very long time".* After the Second World War, Steinhaus was elected a member of some scientific committee. Among the members of this committee there were many poor scientists who were the members of it because of political reasons. Once Steinhaus did not come for the meeting of the committee and he was asked to explain the reason of his absence. He answered: *"I am not going to give any reason of my absence until some others will give reasons for their presence here".* He used to say that *"a computer is an extremely efficient idiot".*

He was an accomplished populariser of mathematics. His book "Mathematical Snapshots" first published in 1938, was translated into many languages. Strangely enough, it was not reissued in Poland between 1957 and 1990!

Stanisław Mazur (1905–1981), a mathematician who offered a goose as a reward for solving one problem, Banach's pupil and friend, was also an excellent mathematician. Like Banach, he did not publish many of his results, but for another reason. Banach had too many ideas and results, whereas Mazur did not like publishing. There is an interesting story about Mazur connected with that subject. Once a new issue of "Zentralblatt" (a journal which published summaries of mathematical papers) arrived to the university library. Mazur took it, looked through, smiled, threw "Zentralblatt" onto the table, and said: *"These results of mine on the theory of convex fields were not so bad, they still haven't got everything".*

One day somebody proposed Mazur the following game: the first player gives the first and the last letter of a word and the second should immediately find a suitable word. Mazur said: *"There's no problem at all".* – "But sometimes it is difficult to find a word. For instance, take the letters

I and C." Mazur immediately answered: "*ilec*" (there is no such word in the Polish language). – "*I'm sorry, what's ilec ?*" – "*By ilec I mean every number divisible by 5*".

For Mazur only two things were interesting: mathematics and communism. Before the war it was not known that he was a member of the Communist Party.

Mazur was 13 years younger than Banach. He started his study when Banach was already a professor. Nevertheless, Banach treated Mazur as a partner. They worked together. Mazur frequently judged Banach's ideas, gave details of proofs.

Other Banach's excellent pupils working in Lvov were Juliusz Paweł Schauder and Władysław Orlicz. In the thirties, Kazimierz Kuratowski, a Warsaw mathematician, came for some years to Lvov. One of Kuratowski's pupils was Ulam.

Stanisław Ulam (known later throughout the world as Stan Ulam) was born in 1909 in Lvov, where he studied and initially worked. Already as a first-year-student he obtained original mathematical results which were soon published. Following an invitation by John von Neumann, one of the greatest mathematicians of the first half of the 20th century, he went to the United States in 1935 and settled there. Among other things, Ulam is most famous for his research in nuclear physics, performed at Los Alamos for 25 years (1943-1967). He was one of the discoverers of the theoretical foundations of the construction of the hydrogen bomb. He had broad scientific interests and obtained important results in various areas of mathematics (set theory, topology, measure theory, group theory, functional analysis, ergodic theory, probability, and game theory) as well as in a number of sciences (technology, computer science, physics, astronomy, and biology). He developed original methods of propulsion of vessels moving above the earth's atmosphere. Ulam died in 1984. His life and work are described in the book "From Cardinals to Chaos", published posthumously at Los Alamos, and in his autobiography "Adventures of a Mathematician".

Another young mathematician, who moved abroad from Lvov before the war, was Mark Kac, well known because of his achievements in probability theory and statistics.

The names of many mathematicians from the Lvov Mathematical School are until now very well known in the world, but for sure the most frequently mentioned is Banach's name. It turned out that Banach is the mathematician (from the whole world) who is mentioned most frequently in the titles of mathematical scientific papers in the 20th century! Banach's name is associated with many important, by now classical theorems: the Hahn-Banach Theorem, the Banach-Steinhaus Theorem, the Banach Open Mapping Theorem, the Banach-Alaoglu Theorem, the Banach Closed Graph Theorem, and the Banach Fixed Point Theorem. And above all, there is the fundamental mathematical concept of a Banach space. What is it?

We learn in school about straight lines, planes, and three-dimensional space. We can describe these geometric objects by means of numbers. Specifically, we can identify the points on a straight line with single real numbers, the points on a plane with pairs of real numbers, and the points in space with triples of real numbers. This idea can be extended to the study of finite sequences of numbers. These sequences can be added, and multiplied by numbers, very much like vectors. In this way we create so-called finite-dimensional spaces. We can – and do – go further. We add, and multiply by constants, numerical-valued functions, by defining the sum of two such functions at a point to be the sum of their values at the point in question. In this we are no longer dealing with a finite-dimensional spaces.

It turned out for a variety of reasons that function spaces are very useful in many investigations and applications. To a large extent, modern mathematics is concerned with the study of general structures, specific models of which have been known for a long time. One advantage of studying a general structure is the economy of thought: a theorem proved for the general structure need not be re-proved for its different models. Moreover, the general proof makes it easier to identify the properties utilized in the course of the proof and thus makes it more transparent. It is paradoxical but true that sometimes the general proof is easier than its particular versions. Moreover, it is frequently useful in unanticipated situations.

But the essential thing is finding the right generalization. Insufficient generality can be too restrictive and a great deal of generality may result in a situation where little can be proved and applied. The space introduced by Banach attests to his genius; he hit the traditional nail on the head.

A space whose elements can be added, and multiplied by numbers, is called a vector space and its elements are called vectors. From the viewpoint of mathematical analysis and its various offshoots, vector spaces (without any additional structure on them) are of relatively little interest. At the beginning of the 20th century one of the greatest mathematicians of the world, David Hilbert, introduced a kind of vector space – now known as Hilbert space – in which one could define perpendicularity. Notwithstanding its tremendous importance and its many applications, the notion of a Hilbert space turned out to be too restrictive for some very significant purposes.

In the early phase of the study of Hilbert space mathematicians introduced in it the notion of a norm, which corresponds, roughly, to the notion of the length of a vector anchored at the origin. However, for some problems the concept turned out to be too general. At this point Banach came up with what turned out to be the ideal structure, namely, the notion of a normed vector space which has the additional property of so-called completness. Roughly speaking, completness means, that if the distance between the elements of an arbitrary sequence tends to zero, then this sequence must have the limit (the elements of the sequence "go somewhere"; in formal language – every sequence satisfying the Cauchy condition is convergent).

A straight line, a plane, a three-dimensional space are the simplest examples of Banach spaces. Generally, more complicated spaces are considered. Some spaces of functions are of particular interest. It is safe to say that by singling out the class of *complete normed vector space* Banach "hit the jackpot". It turned out that the property of completeness was used in an essential way in proving many important theorems.

Banach's great merit was that, in principle, it was thanks to him that the "geometric" way of looking at spaces was initiated. The elements of some general spaces might be functions or number sequences, but when fitted into the structure of a Banach space they were regarded as "points", as the elements of a "space". At times this resulted in remarkable simplification.

The great advantage of Banach space is that, in spite of their abstractions and great generality, they have properties that accord with many intuitive notions associated with the geometries of the plane and of the three-dimensional space. Today, eighty–odd years after its introduction, the notion of a Banach space remains fundamental in many areas of mathematics. The theory of Banach spaces is being developed to this day, and new, interesting, and occasionally surprising results are obtained be many researches. In particular, some really important results were obtained recently by William Timothy Gowers.

Some problems he solved waited for the solution since Banach's times. For his research, Gowers was awarded in 1998 with Fields medal, the most important reward in mathematical world. Moreover, there are many problems related to Banach spaces waiting for a solution.

The name "Banach space" was probably used for the first time by Maurice Fréchet, in 1928. The Lvov mathematician quickly showed the usefulness of the concept by proving in remarkably simple ways many difficult theorems which generalized certain, seemingly even more difficult, special cases. It should be pointed out that the eminent American mathematician Norbert Wiener arrived independently at the idea of Banach space (for a time one spoke of Banach-Wiener spaces), but decided that the relevant axioms implied excessive generality and were impractical from the viewpoint of applications. A few years later, after seeing the splendid uses of Banach spaces, he changed his mind and admitted an error of judgment.

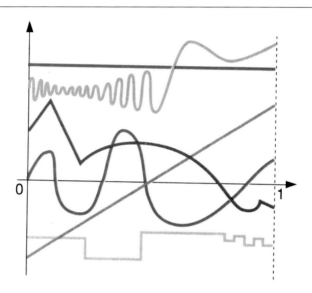

A very important example of a Banach space is the space of continuous functions on a closed interval, say $[0, 1]$, denoted usually by $C([0, 1])$. Its elements are added according to the rule

$$(f \oplus g)(x) = f(x) + g(x)$$

and multiplied by a number according to the rule

$$(a \odot f)(x) = a \cdot f(x)$$

The norm of a function f is defined rather simply as the largest of the values $|f(x)|$:

$$||f|| = \max\{|f(x)| : x \in [0, 1]\}$$

It is not difficult to verify that the space $C([0, 1])$ is a Banach space. But it is impossible to define in it a "reasonable" notion of perpendicularity, it is not a Hilbert space.

Banach and his collaborators made an important contribution to the emergence of the vital area of mathematics known as functional analysis. Functional analysis can be described in a rough and imprecise manner as the study of the properties of certain functions whose domains are various Banach spaces. Functional analysis makes it possible to solve many problems that belong to other areas of mathematics (in particular, problems related to the study of differential equations). The by now classical monograph on functional analysis is Banach's "Linear Operations", published in Polish in 1931. A French translation, "Théorie des opérations linéaires", appeared in 1932. There is an amusing story to the effect that, upon publication, Banach's monograph was displayed in some Lvov bookshops on shelves labelled "Medical Books".

Banach obtained many outstanding results in many other branches of mathematics as well.

A curious and surprising result is a theorem proved in 1924 by Banach and Alfred Tarski about a paradoxical decomposition of the ball. It says that it is possible to break up a ball in the three-dimensional space into a finite number of pieces that can be recombined to form two balls identical with the initial ball. This is a magical proliferation of balls – a doubling of volume! It seems to be an obvious nonsense.

To make this stunt more plausible we point out that it involves the use of very strange pieces. They are nonmeasurable, i.e. they do not have any volume. It does not mean that they have volume equal to 0 or that we do not know how to measure their volumes, it precisely means that do not have volume. We have no idea how they look like. The existence of such strange pieces is guaranteed by one of axioms of set theory, called the axiom of choice. This axiom says, more or less, that given an arbitrary family of sets we can select an element from each of them and form a new set out of the selected elements. For instance, we can form a representation of a school taking one pupil from each class. This seems to be an obvious possibility that inspires no doubts. What is troublesome that its consequences can be absurd. But is a paradoxical decomposition of the ball really so strange?

In 1988 Robert French wrote an article about the construction of the Banach-Tarski decomposition and ended it with the words: *"So much for the theory. Now let's move on to some amusing practical applications. All you need is a sharp knife, a small loaf of bread, a few fish, and a large audience. Then if you go about carefully doing the cuts and reassemblies indicated in this article, who knows where it all might lead."*

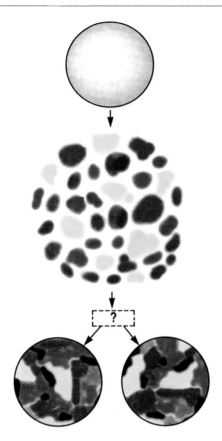

Banach and Tarski proved that it is possible to break up a ball into a finite number of pieces that can be recombined to form two balls identical with the initial ball. However, it is impossible to draw (or precisely describe) such a decomposition, because these pieces do not have any volume. We have no idea how these pieces look like.

Some problems stated in the *Scottish Book* did not require advanced mathematics in its formulation. Particularly elementary there was a question stated by Stanisław Ruziewicz: can one decompose a square into a finite numbers of squares no two the same size? Ruziewicz, who posed this problem in the book, said that he heard the problem from somebody from Krakow. For several years mathematicians in Lvov tried in vain to solve this problem. At last, in 1938 R. Sprague, using an earlier observation by Zbigniew Moroń, showed the construction of the dissection of the square into 55 different squares. Later on several dissections into smaller number of squares were shown. At last the case was definitively closed in 1978 by a Dutchman A. Duijvestijn who decomposed the square into 21 different squares (see the picture) and proved that it is impossible to decompose the square onto 20 or less different squares.

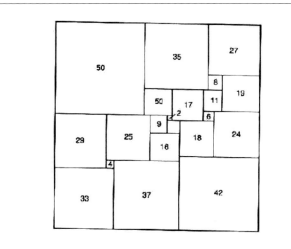

The decomposition of the square into 21 smaller squares,
pairwise different.

An interesting theorem which can be formulated in elementary way is "the sandwich theorem" proved by Banach. The problem was posed by Steinhaus. There are three pairwise disjoint solids (that is, two different solids have no element in common) in the three-dimensional space. Can one halve all of them by means of a single cut? The answer is yes. A consequence is that it is possible to cut a sandwich with butter and ham into two parts each of which contains half of each of the three ingredients. Its proof is advanced and nontrivial.

Another advanced theorem with a difficult proof but with simple formulation is the Borsuk-Ulam theorem about antipodes. The problem was posed by Stan Ulam and solved in 1933 by a great Warsaw mathematician, Karol Borsuk. Formally, in the two-dimensional case it says that for every continuous function defined on a sphere with values in the plane there exists a pair of antipodal points at which it takes on the same value. This theorem has a simple interpretation. When we prick a spherical balloon it collapses and becomes, essentially, a double sheet of rubber. We can say that each point ot the original balloon is now "glued" to some other point on it. The theorem about antipodes asserts that one of these pairs was originally a pair of antipodal points. The flattened balloon is a subset of the plane. We are interested in a continuous transformation which rules out tears. All we did was let the air out of the balloon.

This theorem has also a very curious and surprising geographical consequences: at every moment there are two antipodal points on the face of the Earth with identical temperature and pressure. Such a claim would surprise almost every geographer or climatologist.

The magnificent development of the Lvov Mathematical school was broke by the Second World War. In 1939 Lvov was captured by the Soviet Union. The new government immediately made efforts to destroy the Poles, Polish science and Polish culture in this area. Many people were imprisoned. About two millions of Poles from the east Poland were deported, mainly to Siberia and Kazakhstan. The communists were particularly interested in deporting the officers of the army, the lawyers, the writers and the scientists.

Banach was not arrested and not deported. He was even allowed to continue his work at the university. Perhaps it was because that he was in fact really interested only in mathematics, perhaps because of the support of Mazur (as then his communist outlook on life became widely known), perhaps of the support of Soviet mathematicians he collaborated with.

In 1941 Hitler's soldiers took Lvov for 4 years. Then Banach's situation became worse. He was not longer allowed to lecture at the university. He lived in extremely difficult conditions.

When the war finished and it was finally decided that Lvov would be a part of the Soviet Union, Banach planned to go to Krakow, where he would have taken a Chair of mathematics at the Jagiellonian University, but a few days before the removal, in 1945 he died, age 53.

The story of the Lvov Mathematical School ended together with the Second World War. During the war, other excellent Polish mathematicians died. In Lvov, Nazis killed Juliusz Schauder and Herman Auerbach . Several others frequent guests of the *Scottish Café* also did not survive. Also, Stanisław Zaremba and Witold Wilkosz in Krakow died. A young very talented mathematician, Józef Marcinkiewicz from Vilnius, who spent some years in Lvov, was murdered together with other Polish army officers in Katyń by Stalin's regiment.

Other excellent members of the Lvov School moved from there. Steinhaus came to Wrocław (Breslau) which because of the Jałta agreement was taken from Germany and included to Poland. Mazur was in Warsaw. He has got an important position because of his party connections, but he held this position for a very short time, because he never took the trouble to answer letters. He was interested in mathematics above all, so he continued his research. Orlicz moved to Poznań. Andrzej Turowicz turned up at the monastery in Tyniec, close to Krakow, and became a priest and a monk. Otto Nikodym and, as was told earlier, Ulam and Kac emigrated to the United States before the war and if they even planned to go back to Poland, because of the war they definitively decided to stay there for good.

Banach was buried at Lychakov Cemetery in Lvov. In 1985 the Polish Mathematical Society started procedures for the transfer of Banach's body to Poland. This raised a difficult question: w here should Banach's tomb be? In Lvov, the city of the Lvov Mathematical School, where he worked and became famous? Or in a city in present-day Poland, where many people, particularly his family, would have the opportunity to put flowers on his grave? At any rate, the attempts of the Polish Mathematical Society have proved unsuccessful.

We conclude with one more anecdote. The International Congresses of Mathematicians take place every four years. Hosting a congress is a great honour for the country entrusted with its organization. The 1983 International Congress of Mathematicians took place in Warsaw. A few foreign mathematicians found out that there is a street in Warsaw called Banach Street, and this is the last stop on a certain trolley line. Curious about Banach Street, they got on the trolley, got off at the last stop, and were confronted by a sizable empty area. They arrived at the unanimous conclusion that what they were facing was not "Banach street" but rather a "Banach space".

Now, in Lvov, Akademic Street is named by Shevchenko. The *Scottish Café* is a usual restaurant, "Desertnyi" bar[4]. There are no marble tables. Guidebooks about Lvov published in the Soviet Union do not mention the café and Lvov mathematicians from the period before WWII. However, former citizen of Lvov, now spread out almost everywhere in the world, asked about the *Scottish Café* answer immediately: "Ah, this café, where those mathematicians used to meet..."

> Translation prepared by the authors with the use of many fragments translated by *Abe Shenitzer* as *Abe Shenitzer* translated the authors' book "Mathematical Diamonds" [53].

---

[4]This article was written in the nineties; at present there is a bank office.

Chapter 7

The Scottish Book[1]

Marek Kordos[2] (Warsaw)

Mathematicians work in a rather specific way and, quite often, they require specific conditions to work efficiently. Among these conditions we should mention an appropriate, mainly public place with a sufficient supply of all kinds of beverages. In other words, something we might call a café. The Lvov School of Mathematics of the pre-war period was formed by two such neighbouring places: the Scottish Café (Café Szkocka) and Café Roma. Nevertheless, posterity will only be aware of the former due to a lucky investment by its owner.[3] The investment took the form of a thick, carefully bound (and equally carefully attached to the table) notebook, where the gentlemen mathematicians could write their precious ideas, thus misusing fewer paper napkins. The gentlemen mathematicians liked the idea and thus a unique piece of mathematical literature came into existence – a collection of more than 193 random mathematics problems being the result of what might be called a form of social life. It should be noticed that both the problems and the answers or comments were written in various languages (like English or Russian) that happened to occur to the authors at the moment of writing. Sometimes the formulation of a problem was followed by the promise of a prize for the solution. This could be five beers or a live goose. The prize never failed to be delivered to the winner.

---

[1]Slightly condensed translation of an article from *Delta* (No. 9 (221), pp. 11–13, 1994) with permission of the author and the editorial office. Translated by the author.

[2]See biographical note B-12.

[3]It appears that it was not the owner of the Café but Banach's wife who personally invested in the notebook.

Stefan Banach was the first to enter a problem in the *Book* on 17 July 1935. The last problem, number 193, was due to Hugo Steinhaus and it is dated 31 May 1941. The total number of problems was actually greater than 193, since the numbering was at times repetitive. For instance, the numbers 10.1, 15.1 or 17.1 are used more than once. Most problems, though not all, have been solved. In some cases the solution was not a mere intellectual exercise or sport, for it marked the beginning of a new direction of research.

I mentioned that the *Scottish Book* was written in different languages. It should be clear, however, that the prevailing language was Polish. And the following is an example of a loss due only to our own tradition. Anyone who today wants to reach for the *Scottish Book* will find it only in the English language! It was published by... the Boston branch of the Birkhäuser publishing house [26]. The publication was edited by R. Daniel Mauldin although Polish mathematicians had a major input into it. The Book contains – besides some comments about earlier publications of the problems it contains – five lectures delivered at a conference on the *Book* (by Stanisław Ulam[4] Marek Kac, Antoni Zygmund, Paul Erdös and Andrzej Granas) and has all of the original problems, with very interesting comments by more than fifty mostly Polish mathematicians. I am writing about the *Book* and describing it here because most readers may not have the chance to see it firsthand. That is a pity because they would then have the chance of seeing the facsimile of several pages of the original *Scottish Book*. Anyway, let's stop whetting the appetite.

I shall now quote six problems drawn from the *Scottish Book*. Three of them have been solved, the other three have not.

Problem 152 (Steinhaus)

Prizes:
* *For computing the frequency: 100 g of caviar.*
* *For proof of the existence of frequency: a small beer.*
* *For a counter-example: a cup of coffee.*

6 November 1936.

A circle with radius 1 contains at least two points with integer coordinates (x, y) and at most five such points. If one translates this circle by vectors $n\mathbf{w}$ ($n=1,2,3,...$), where $\mathbf{w} = (a, b)$ with both coordinates irrational and such that their ratio a/b is also an irrational number, then numbers 2, 3,

---

[4]See biographical note B-20.

4 [of points with both coordinates being integers] will appear an infinite number of times. What is the frequency of their appearing as n goes to infinity? Does it exist?

Solution

The solution of this problem (100 g of caviar worth) follows from a general theorem on equipartition, which was known to Steinhaus when he entered the problem into the *Book*. I would rather invite the reader to justify a simpler and more ingenious approach: if a unit square is divided into parts by the arcs of unit circles drawn from the vertices of the square and the parts obtained are called as on the figure below, then the sum of the areas of the parts called P_i will be equal to the frequency of the occurrence of i points with both coordinates being integers in the unit circle. For the lazy among us there is a simpler question. Prove that the frequency is:

* For 2: $\quad 4 - \sqrt{3} - \frac{2}{3}\pi$
* For 3: $\quad 2\sqrt{3} - 4 + \frac{\pi}{3}$
* For 4: $\quad 1 - \sqrt{3} + \frac{\pi}{3}$

Obviously, it is also possible to compute areas of the figures P_2, P_3 and P_4.

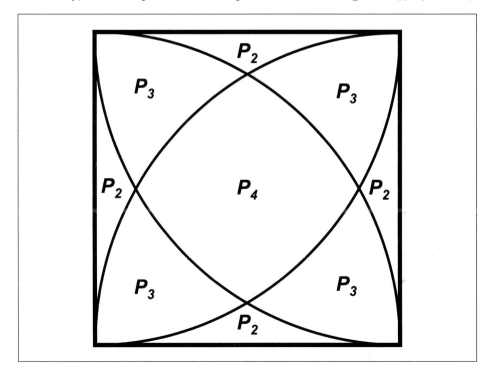

Problem 44 (Steinhaus)

A continuous function $z = f(x, y)$ describes a surface with the property that two straight lines lying entirely on the surface pass through each of its points. Prove that the surface is a hyperbolic paraboloid. Prove the same without the assumption of continuity.

Solution

I owe the reader an explanation of the term "hyperbolic paraboloid". This is a surface that resembles a cavalry saddle and is generated by a parabola sliding with its vertex along another parabola lying in a plane perpendicular to the plane of the first and such that its axis is parallel to the first plane. Moreover, the first parabola is to be thought as having its arms directed downwards, while the second has its arms directed upwards. It may seem doubtful whether indeed two straight lines do pass through each point of the surface. Well, such doubts seem to create a great opportunity to raise one's mathematical conscience to a higher level.

In the *Scottish Book* the problem is followed by a **Note:**

> *The problem has been solved in the positive by Stefan Banach – also without the assumption of continuity. The proof is based on the following observation: any two straight lines lying on such a surface either intersect or their projections onto the plane xy are parallel.*
>
> *30 July 1935.*
>
> *I recommend following Banach's way.*

Problem 59 (Ruziewicz)

Can a square be decomposed into a finite number of squares each of a different size?

Solution

The complete solution can be found both in the journal *Delta* [57] and in the *Mathematical Snapshots* by Hugo Steinhaus [79]. The solution in *Delta* is more complete, although the newest Polish edition of the *Mathematical Snapshots* appeared in the same year, i.e. 11 years after the ultimate solution of the problem. A square can be divided into 21 squares of different size and no smaller number is sufficient, as A.J.W. Duijvestijn proved. The side of the largest square is $\frac{25}{56}$ of the side of the original square, whereas the side of the smallest is $\frac{1}{56}$ the size of the original side.

Problem 60 (Ruziewicz)

Given a positive number epsilon, can the surface of a unit sphere be divided into finitely many connected and pairwise congruent components so that the diameter of each is less than ϵ?

Solution

The problem may change depending on what we choose the component boundaries to be: (a) spherical polygons, (b) curves of finite length, or (c) arbitrary sets of null area. If the answer is not always positive, it would be interesting to find the least value of epsilon for which a required decomposition exists. In 1979, M.J. Wenninger produced a nontrivial decomposition of the sphere surface into 120 congruent spherical triangles. Can this number be increased without making the triangles too thin, for instance, if we require that each side of a triangle be less than $\pi/3$?

Again, both the *Mathematical Snapshots* and *Delta* mention another problem:

Problem 19 (Ulam)

Must a solid of homogeneous density which can float on water in an arbitrary position be a sphere?

Solution

No general solution is known, although some very particular cases have been solved. These particular cases include density zero, where the problem comes down to finding a solid lying on the horizontal plane in arbitrary position (the "zero" is treated as the limit case), and here the answer is positive. The second particular case corresponds to a two-dimensional setting, which cannot be considered a normal situation either. Here for density zero the answer is positive but, e.g., for density $1/2$ there are many solutions other than for the sphere (= circle). A whole series of them has been provided by Auerbach in 1938. They are figures such that each secant which halves the perimeter also halves the area.

If you are in need of a result for an arbitrary dimension, here it is: if the solid is centrally symmetric, then – at density $1/2$ – it must be a sphere. Hence there is no solution for the general case.

Here is a similar problem formulated just a few years ago:

Problem *** (Lipniacki, Wojciechowski)

For what quantity of liquid in a bottle is the centre of gravity at its lowest position?

Solution

The problem has practical significance, namely, when to stop drinking on a trip! I shall not present the solution here, although I know what it is. Let the reader enjoy solving the problem too.

This example may suggest that the problems in the *Scottish Book* are shear entertainment. This is not so, however. It's just me choosing the simplest. Here is another. This time it uses very scientific language, which comes as no surprise if we consider the long list of authors.

Problem 10.1 (Mazur, Auerbach, Ulam, Banach)

Theorem. If $K(n)$ $(n=1,2,3,...)$ is a sequence of convex bodies such that each of them has a diameter smaller than or equal to a and the sum of their volumes is smaller than or equal to b, then there exists a cube of diameter $c = f(a,b)$ with the property that all the bodies can be disjointedly collocated within it.

Corollary. A kilogram of potatoes can be collocated within a bag of finite dimensions.

Problem. Determine the function $c = f(a,b)$.

Solution

To this day the problem, seen as the problem of finding the least such function, remains unsolved. The authors of partial solutions usually looked for a cuboid rather than for a cube. In 1957, Kosiński estimated its sides – for the k-dimensional case – at

$$3a, 3a, ..., 3a, a + k!\,\frac{b}{a^{k-1}}.$$

Ten years later Moon and Moser obtained a different result (only for $k=3$, 4, 5,...):

$$2a, 2a, ..., 2a, 2\left(a + k!\,\frac{b}{a^{k-1}}\right).$$

The only certain fact today is that in the k-dimensional space, for k at least 3,

$$f(a,b) \leq \sqrt{k} \min\left\{ \max\left\{3a, a + k!\, \frac{b}{a^{k-1}}\right\},\, 2\max\left\{a, a + k!\, \frac{b}{a^{k-1}}\right\}\right\}.$$

Appendix[5]

The enclosed facsimiles of the first two pages of the *Scottish Book* include the following problems:[6]

1. Problem by Banach (17 July 1935)

a) When can a metric space (possibly of type (B)) be so metrised that it will become complete and compact, and so that all the sequences converging originally, should also converge in the new metric?

b) Can, for example, the space $[C_0]$ be so metrised?

2. Problem by Banach-Ulam

a) Can one define, in every compact metric space E, a measure (finitely additive) so that Borel sets which are congruent should have equal measure?

b) Suppose $E = E_1 + E_2 + \cdots + E_n$, and $E_1 \cong E_2 \cong \cdots \cong E_n$ and $\{E_n\}$ are disjoint? Then we write $E_i = \frac{1}{n}E$. Can it occur that $\frac{1}{n}E \cong \frac{1}{m}E$ $(n \neq m)$, if we assume that $\frac{1}{n}E$ are Borel sets and E is compact?

3. Theorem by Banach-Ulam

It is proved very simply that a compact set cannot be congruent to a proper subset of itself.

4. Theorem by Schreier

If $\{\xi_k\}$ is a bounded sequence, summable by the first mean to ξ, then almost every subsequence of it is also summable by the first mean to ξ.

---

[5]Materials provided by the Banach family from their private collection to supplement Professor M. Kordos' article.

[6]This translation is based on the English manuscript of *Scottish Book*, presumed to be by Stanisław Ulam, from the Archive of the Mathematics Faculty Library of Wrocław University.

Facsimile of page 1 of the *Scottish Book* manuscript.

Facsimile of page 2 of the *Scottish Book* manuscript.

5. Problem by Mazur

Definition: A sequence $\{\xi_k\}$ is asymptotically convergent to ξ, if there exists a sub-sequence of density 1 convergent to ξ.

Theorem by Mazur

This notion is not equivalent in the domain of all sequences to any Töplitz method. How is it in the domain of bounded sequences?

6. Problem by Mazur, Orlicz (Prize: Bottle of wine, S. Mazur)

Is a matrix, finite in each row and invertible (in a 1 to 1 way), equivalent to a normal matrix?

Chapter 8

The New Scottish Book

Roman Duda[1] (Wrocław)

The mathematics that originated in Wrocław after 1945 (since that year a part of Poland) had a strong connection to Lvov. Three of its four pioneers had spent a considerable amount of time in Lvov: Hugo Steinhaus received *venia legendi* there in 1917 and lived his most productive years there until 1941, Edward Marczewski spent the first two years of the war in Lvov, i.e., from 1939 to 1941, and Bronisław Knaster was there for the duration of the war from 1939 to 1945. Only the fourth, Władysław Ślebodziński, was never in Lvov. He worked in Poznań before the war, completed his academic studies in Warsaw and spent most of the war as a prisoner in Auschwitz. Of these four the first to arrive in Wrocław was E. Marczewski [55]. Following the collapse of the Old Town enclave during the Warsaw uprising he came to Wrocław in October 1944 (as a political prisoner), survived the siege of the city, and in May 1945 joined Professor S. Kulczyński's Cultural- Scientific Group there. He stayed on in Wrocław and became the organiser and one of the leaders of a new center of mathematics (German mathematicians left the city before the siege and the German Institute of Mathematics had been destroyed by fire during the siege [70]). He was a man of great energy who cared very much that the new center would be a continuation of what he considered to be the best in Polish mathematics, namely, the Warsaw and Lvov traditions [67]. In pursuit of this goal he attracted pioneers and looked for potential successors who would be able to continue work.

---

[1]See biographical note B-8.

As instances of Marczewski's efforts were his decisions to continue with
the Lvov *Scottish Book* (which was brought to Wrocław by Łucja Banach,
wife of Stefan Banach, as part of her luggage, after she and her son Stefan were deported from Lvov in 1946), and to establish a new mathematics
periodical. The first problems were entered into the *New Scottish Book* by
H. Steinhaus at the beginning of July, 1946. These had a symbolic status
in that he had entered the last problem in the Lvov *Book* (193, 31 May,
1941) closing it, as it were, and starting the new Wrocław *Book* five years
later. Several days after that Gustav Choquet, at that time an employee
of the French Institute in Kraków [59] entered two new problems. Subsequent ones were entered by E. Marczewski, B. Knaster, and H. Steinhaus
in 1946, and also in that year by an illustrious group of the best Polish
mathematicians who had survived the war: A. Alexiewicz, S. Gołąb, A.
Mostowski, W. Orlicz, W. Sierpiński, R. Sikorski, J. Szarski, T. Ważewski,
Z. Zahorski and also others on the occasion of the Fourth Convention of
Polish Mathematicians held in Wrocław from 12 to 14 December, 1946.
Altogether 35 problems were entered that year and prizes were offered for
solutions to some of them. For example, for solutions to two of his problems
G. Choquet promised a bottle of champagne, to be consumed in Paris, if
the answers were positive, and a bottle of Bordeaux if negative. V. Jarnik
offered "Plzenské pivo" (a Czech beer) in a quantity of 300 litres (!) for a
negative answer to his problem number 33. Later H. Steinhaus promised a
ration coupon for meat, at that time an attractive prize, for a solution to
his problem number 175 (1952). (The prize was won by R. Sikorski who
then insisted it had to be redeemed in Warsaw, which was no doubt more
difficult than finding the solution in the first place.) For a solution to his so-
called "Easter" problem number 269 (1955) H. Steinhaus offered an Easter
egg (decorated by him personally) as the prize.

After an auspicious beginning the *New Scottish Book* experienced a few
very lively decades, as witnessed by the large numbers of problems, comments and solutions that were entered in it. In the absence of a repository
for it like the *Scottish Café* in Lvov, the Wrocław *Book* resided at the Mathematics Seminary of the University and Polytechnic, which was for many
years the center of Wrocław's mathematical life. Later it was kept in the Library of Wrocław University's Mathematics Institute. The *Book's* pioneers
and caretakers made sure it was readily available for use and were always
especially ready to put it in front of any mathematician visiting Wrocław.

From 1946 to 1955 some 286 problems were entered into the *Book*, but
its best decade was from 1956 to 1965 when 464 were entered. Then in

the decade from 1966 to 1975 157 problems were entered. Starting in 1976 (notably the year of E. Marczewski's death) interest in the *Book* and in its significance began to decline, as manifested by the rapidly decreasing number of problems and comments that were being entered in it. Only one problem was entered in 1982, and none during the next four years, and finally in 1987 K. Głazek added the last two problems that he had presented to no avail during some conferences; he received no response to them in the *Book* either. Thus the *New Scottish Book* lasted for over forty years and it had a dynamic and expansive quality in contrast to the *Scottish Book* from Lvov whose existence was shorter, limited to the years from 1935 to 1941, and whose dynamism declined relatively quickly [56]. During the time of its existence altogether 968 problems were entered into the *New Book*, an average rate of 24 annually (its Lvov predecessor had 193, an average of 27 annually). In reality, however, it was somewhat more than that because some problems consisted of several questions, and there were also ones that were not numbered. Unlike its predecessor [26], the *New Book* has not so far been more extensively analyzed and studied. Nevertheless, it may be confidently asserted that for four decades it was a very integral part of mathematical life in Wrocław, a support and inspiration for many and a contemporary chronicle for all.

Another of E. Marczewski's initiatives was the founding of a new periodical. This was a bigger challenge than purchasing a thick notebook for the *New Book*, but already in 1948 the first volume of *Colloquium Mathematicum* made its appearance with four pioneers as its editors. In the same year *Studia Mathematica* was reborn in Wrocław (the editors of the first Wrocław volume, which was also the tenth sequential volume, were H. Steinhaus, E. Marczewski and B. Knaster). em Studia confined itself to "the theory of operators and its applications", that is to functional analysis, whereas Marczewski wanted his *Colloquium* to serve all of the branches of mathematics that might appear in Wrocław. The new periodical styled itself after the tradition of the Warsaw *Fundamenta Mathematicae* and the Lvov *eStudia Mathematica* but also possessed its own individual characteristics. To the extent the others presumed to be specialized [11, 54], *Colloquium* took on a more general character. Moreover, *Colloquium* contained a chronicle section *Chronique*, which today is a veritable storehouse of information about Polish mathematical life during those times. It also had a section devoted solely to problems *Problemès* which survived for many years and was used to revisit problems previously formulated in articles published in *Colloquium*, and included some of the more interesting ones from the *New*

Scottish Book. It also contained letters to the editor, various comments and solutions to problems, partial or complete, and if complete a note that a particular problem had been solved.

A more detailed review and discussion of these problems, their destiny and influence on mathematics, is beyond the scope of this article. Let us only note, however, that the *Problemès* section survived until 1990 and during that time published 1384 problems, of which about a fourth came from the *New Scottish Book.* The most prolific, in that respect, was the 1948-1972 period during which a total of 312 problems came from the *Book.* Subsequently, for a time, only single problems were abstracted from it until 1982 when the last two were published in Volume 46. Altogether 335 problems from the *New Scottish Book* appeared in *Colloquium Mathematicum.*

Anecdotically let us note problem P 1217 (Q) in *Colloquium Mathematicum* 44 (1981) which went as follows:

> S. Manhart (Sany) P 1217
>
> (Q). Consider a random walk of extreme element $H_{int} = H(t)$ of the solid category S. The process develops within a rectilinear 3-cell N whose boundary ∂N is connected and closed. Estimate the expectation of $\tau_\epsilon = inf\, t > 0 : H(t) \notin N$.
>
> Letter of January 4, 1982:

> P 1217 (Q), R1. In the Manhart case, τ_ϵ turned to be $2^5 + 1$. In other cases the problem is still open.
>
> Letter of February 6, 1982

This is mathematical gibberish, not easily identified as such by a non-mathematician, but it has the following hidden message: The alleged S. Manhart (Sany) is S. Hartman (Nysa) whose supposed letter of 4 January reminds the reader that since that day he is on "a random walk (...) inside a rectilinear 3-dimensional cell N, whose boundary ∂N is connected and closed" in the internment camp in Nysa . The time of his internment was to be deduced from "$\tau_\epsilon = inf\, t > 0 : H(t) \notin N$". In an update it could be noted that in his case the time was 25+1 (=33 days) but "in other cases the problem is still open".

The letter made it past the censors and French friends in Paris understood the problem....

Nothing lasts for ever, but it is also possible to point to some more direct and proximate causes that led to the demise of the *New Book* and in its footsteps likewise the disappearance of the section *Problemès* in *Colloquium Mathematicum:*

1. The passing in the seventies of the generation of pioneers.

2. The move by the Mathematics Institute of Wrocław University away from its shared quarters with the Mathematics department of the Wrocław Polytechnic, resulting in a splintering of a hitherto common life of these two bodies.

3. The evolution of the Mathematics Faculty of the Polytechnic into the Mathematical Institute of Wrocław Polytechnic, a progression from which was the establishment by the Polytechnic of its own mathematics courses as part of the Faculty of Basic Technology.

4. A diminution of the importance of the Polish Mathematical Society and specifically the reduction of the number and frequency of its meetings and conferences.

5. The tendency to a more internal focus by both Institutes leading to a lessening of common interests in mathematics.

Today the *New Scottish Book*, in the form of three thick notebooks containing a multitude of entries attesting to its onetime frequent use, is a historical relic carefully preserved in the Library of the Mathematical Institute of Wrocław University. It is an important document and record of the work of the Wrocław mathematicians in the years from 1945 to 1987 and of the colleagues who visited them during that time. It further merits to be well remembered and studied because Wrocław mathematics was then widely known and influential in some world centers of mathematics.

(Translated by *John Greczek*)

Selected Bibliography in English and French

[1] Sheldon Axler, "Review of *Through a Reporter's Eyes: The Life of Stefan Banach*" by Roman Kałuża, *Am. Math. Monthly* **104**, 577–579 (1997).

[2] Stefan Banach, *Rachunek różniczkowy i całkowy* (Differential and Integral Calculus), vol. **1** (Zakład Narodowy im. Ossolińskich, Lvov 1929), vol. **2** (Książnica-Atlas, Lvov, 1930). Russian trans.: *Differential and Integral Calculus* (Fizmatgiz 1958; Nauka, Moscow, 1966, 1972, 1986). Hungarian trans.: *Differenciál és Integrálszámítás* (Tankönyvkiadó, Budapest 1967, 1969, 1971, 1975).

[3] Stefan Banach, *Théorie des opérations linéaires*, Monografie Matematyczne (Mathematical Monographs) vol. **1** (Fundusz Kultury Narodowej, Warszawa, 1932). This is in an extended version of the Polish edition of *Teorja operacyj. Tom 1. Operacje linjowe* (Theory of Operations. Vol. 1: Linear Operations) (Kasa im. Mianowskiego, Warszawa, 1931). Other reprints in French: Hafner Publ., New York, 1932, 1948; Chelsea Publ., New York, 1932, 1955, 1963, 1978, 1988, 1999; Jacques Gabay, Sceaux (France), 1993; also reprinted in Ref. [5]. English trans.: *Theory of Linear Operations* (North-Holland, Amsterdam–New York–Oxford–Tokyo, 1987). Russian trans.: *Theory of Linear Operations* (R&C Dynamics, Izhevsk 2001 (3rd ed.)). Ukrainian trans.: *A Course in Functional Analysis* (Radianska Shkola, Kiev, 1948).

[4] Stefan Banach, *Mechanics*, Monografie Matematyczne (Mathematical Monographs) vol. **24** (Warszawa–Wrocław, 1951). This a translation from Polish of *Mechanika w zakresie szkół akademickich* (Mechanics – In the Scope of Academic Studies), part 1 – Monografie Matematyczne vol. **8**, part 2 – Monografie Matematyczne vol. **9** (Warsaw–Lvov–Wilno 1938).

[5] Stefan Banach, *Oeuvres avec des commentaires* (Collected works of Stefan Banach with comments), vol. **1** edited by A. Alexiewicz, M. Altman, S. Hartman, E. Marczewski,) S. Mazur, W. Orlicz, R. Sikorski
and H. Steinhaus, vol. **2** edited by C. Bessaga, S. Mazur, W. Orlicz,
A. Pełczyński, S. Rolewicz and W. Żelazko (Polish Scientific Publ.
PWN, Warsaw, 1967, 1979).

[6] Krzysztof Ciesielski, "Lost Legends of Lvov 1: The Scottish Café",
Math. Intelligencer **9**, No. 4, 36–37 (1987).

[7] Krzysztof Ciesielski, "Lost Legends of Lvov 2: Banach's Grave", *Math.
Intelligencer* **10**, No. 1, 50–51 (1988).

[8] Krzysztof Ciesielski, "On some details of Stefan Banach's life", *Opuscula Mathematica* **13**, 71–74 (1993).

[9] Krzysztof Ciesielski and Zdzisław Pogoda, "Conversation with Andrzej
Turowicz", *Math. Intelligencer* **10**, No. 4, 13–20 (1988).

[10] Roman Duda, "The discovery of Banach spaces", in: *History of Mathematics in Poland*, Proc. of the First Joint Intern. Meeting of Am.
Math. Soc. and Polish Math. Soc. (July 31 – August 3, 2007, Warsaw),
pp. 37–46 (2007).

[11] Roman Duda, "Fundamenta Mathematicae and the Warsaw school of
mathematics", in: C. Goldstein, J. Gray, J. Ritter (eds.), "L'Europe
mathématique - Mythes, histoires, identitités", Paris 1996, s. 479-498.

[12] Jean Dieudonné, *History of Functional Analysis,* (North-Holland, Amsterdam–New York–Oxford, 1981).

[13] Nelson Dunford, Jacob T. Schwarz, *Linear Operators, Part I: General
Theory* (Interscience, New York 1958).

[14] Mitchell Feigenbaum, "Reflections of the Polish Masters: An Interview
with Stan Ulam and Mark Kac", *Los Alamos Science* **3**, No. 3, 54–65
(1982).

[15] Rolf Haftmann, "Zum 100. Geburtstag von Stefan Banach" (Stefan
Banach's 100th Anniversary), *Wiss. Z. Tech. Univ. Chemnitz* **34**, 9–18
(1992).

[16] D. Henderson, "Banach's Space: Lviv and the Scottish Café", *Cond.
Matt. Phys.* **7**, No. 4 (40), 679–682 (2004).

[17] Graham Hoare and Nick Lord, "Stefan Banach (1892–1945): A Commemoration of His Life and Work", *Math. Gazette* **79**, 456–470 (1995).

[18] Mark Kac, *Enigmas of Chance. An Autobiography* (Harper & Row,
New York, 1985).

[19] Roman Kałuża, *Through a Reporter's Eyes: The Life of Stefan Banach* (Birkäuser, Boston, 1996, 2005) and, in Japanese, *Banacha to*

Pōrando Sūgaku (Banach and Polish mathematics) (Springer Mathematics Club). These are translations from Polish of *Stefan Banach* (GZ Publ., Warsaw, 1992).

[20] Janusz Kowalski, "Polish Mathematical Society", *European Math. Soc. Newsletter*, No. 54, 24–29 (2004).

[21] Kazimierz Kuratowski, *A Half Century of Polish Mathematics: Remembrances and Reflections* (Pergamon Press, Oxford and Polish Scientific Publ. PWN, Warsaw, 1980). This is a translation from Polish of *Pół wieku matematyki polskiej 1920–1970* (Wiedza Powszechna, Warsaw, 1973).

[22] Mary Grace Kuzawa, *Modern Mathematics: The Genesis of a School in Poland* (College and University Press, New Haven, 1968).

[23] S. Lal, "Cardan and Banach: a comparative study", *Math. Ed.* **5** (2), 99–102 (1989).

[24] Lech Maligranda, *Stefan Banach* (in English), in: *The Princeton Companion to Mathematics*, ed. William Timothy Gowers *et al.* (Princeton University Press 2008), p.809-811.

[25] Edward Marczewski, "Sur l'oeuvre scientifique de Stefan Banach II. Théorie des fonctions réeles et théorie de la mesure", *Colloquium Math.* **1**, 93–102 (1947).

[26] R. Daniel Mauldin (ed.), *The Scottish Book: Mathematics from the Scottish Café* (Birkäuser, Boston, 1981).

[27] Ludmila Nosareva, "Matematicheskaya relikvia rodom iz Lvova" (A Mathematical Relic from Lvov) (in Russian), *Zerkalo Nedeli*, No. 26 (401), (2002).

[28] J.J. O'Connor and E.F. Robertson, "Stefan Banach", in: *MacTutor History of Mathematics*, e-print at `www-history.mcs.st-andrews.ac.uk/Biographies/Banach.html` (2000).

[29] Władysław Orlicz, "Sur l'oeuvre scientifique de Stefan Banach I. Théorie des opérations et théorie des séries orthogonales", *Colloquium Math.* **1**, 81–92 (1947).

[30] Józef Piórek, "Polish Mathematical Society", *European Math. Soc. Newsletter*, No. 32, 17–18 (1999).

[31] Hugo Steinhaus, "Souvenir de Stefan Banach", *Colloquium Math.* **1**, 74–80 (1948).

[32] Hugo Steinhaus, "Stefan Banach" (in English), *Studia Mathematica*, Special Series No. 1, 7–15 (1963).

[33] Hugo Steinhaus, *Mathematics is the Mediator Between Spirit and Matter* (in Russian) (Binom – Laboratorya Znanij, 2005). This is a translation from Polish of *Między duchem a materią pośredniczy matematyka* (*ditto*) (Polish Scientific Publ. PWN, Warsaw–Wrocław, 2000).

[34] Wacław Szybalski, "Maintenance of Human-Fed Live Lice in the Laboratory and Production of Weigl's Exanthematous Typhus Vaccine", in: Proceedings of the EPA-APS Symposium on *Maintenance of Human, Animal, and Plant Pathogen Vectors* (Nov 10, 1998, Las Vegas, Nevada); ed. K. Maramorosch, F. Mahmood, pp. 161–180 (Science Publ., Enfield, USA, 1999).

[35] Wacław Szybalski, "The Genius of Rudolf Stefan Weigl" (1883–1957), a Lvovian Microbe Hunter and Breeder – In Memoriam, in: Programme and Abstracts of the International Weigl Conference on *Microorganisms in Pathogenesis and their Drug Resistance* (Sept 11–14, 2003, Lvov, Ukraine); ed. R.Stoik *et al.*, pp. 10–31 (Spolom Publ., Lvov, Ukraine, 2003); also e-prints at `www.lwow.home.pl/Weigl/in-memoriam.html`, `www.lwow.home.pl/tyfus.html`, `www.lwow.home.pl/weigl.html`

[36] Jacob David Tamarkin,, "Banach on Linear Operations" (A review of Ref. [3]), *Bull. Amer. Math. Soc.* **40**, 13–16 (1934).

[37] Stanisław Ulam, "Stefan Banach (1892–1945)", *Bull. Amer. Math. Soc.* **52**, 600–603 (1946).

[38] Stanisław Ulam, *The Scottish Book: a Collection of Problems* (Los Alamos, 1957).

[39] Stanisław Ulam, *Adventures of a Mathematician* (USP, Berkeley, USA, 1976, 1991).

[40] Norbert Wiener, *I am a Mathematician* (Doubleday, New York 1956).

[41] L.C. Young, "A review of *Théorie des opérations linéaires* by S. Banach", *Math. Gazette* **18**, 206–207 (1934).

[42] Wiesław Żelazko, "Stefan Banach (1892–1945)" (in English), *European Math. Society Newsletter* **5**, 23 (1992).

[43] — "Obituary: Stefan Banach" (in Russian), *Uspehi Matem. Nauk* **1**, 13–16 (1946).

[44] — "Obituary: Stefan Banach" (in French), *Colloquium Math.* **1**, 68–73 (1947).

Selected Bibliography in Polish

[45] Zygmunt Albert, *Kaźń profesorów lwowskich – lipiec 1941* (Massacre of the Lvov Professors – July, 1941) (Wrocław University Publ., Wrocław, 1989).

[46] Marian Albiński, "Wspomnienia o Banachu i Wilkoszu" (Reminiscences of Banach and Wilkosz), *Wiadomości Matematyczne* **19**, 133–135 (1976).

[47] Andrzej Alexiewicz, *Analiza funkcjonalna* (Functional Analysis) (Polish Scientific Publ. PWN, Warsaw, 1969).

[48] Stefan Banach, *Wstęp do teorii funkcji rzeczywistych* (An Introduction to the Theory of Real Functions), Monografie Matematyczne (Mathematical Monographs) vol. **17**, Warsaw–Wrocław, 1951.

[49] Feliks Barański, "Lwowskie wspomnienia o Stefanie Banachu" (Lvovian Reminiscences of Stefan Banach), *Opuscula Mathematica* **13**,55–57 (1993).

[50] Marcin Braun, "Cudowne rozmnażanie kul" (The Marvelous Multiplication of Spheres), *Wiedza i Życie*, No. 5, 28–30 (1999).

[51] Krzysztof Ciesielski, "Śladami Banacha we Lwowie" (In the Footsteps of Banach in Lvov), *Matematyka,* **45**, No. 2, 90–95 (1992).

[52] Krzysztof Ciesielski, "Recenzja książki pt. 'Stefan Banach' Romana Kałuży" (Review of Book on *Stefan Banach* by Roman Kałuża), *Wiadomości Matematyczne* **30**, 144–147 (1993).

[53] Krzysztof Ciesielski, Zdzisław Pogoda, "Mathematical Diamonds", Prószyński i S-ka, Warszawa, 1997;

[54] Roman Duda, "Fundamenta Mathematicae, Studia Mathematica, Acta Arithmetica - pierwsze trzy specjalistyczne czasopisma matematyczne", (Fundamenta Mathematicae, Studia Mathematica, Acta Arithmetica – First Specialistic Mathematical Journals), *Zeszyty Naukowe Politechniki Śląskiej, Matematyka-Fizyka* 76, 1995, s. 47-80;

[55] Roman Duda, "Ślązacy z wyboru – pionierzy matematyki w powojennym Wrocławiu" (Silesians by Choice – Pioneers of Mathematics in

Postwar Wrocław), in: M. Hałub, A. Mańko-Matysiak (red.), *Śląska Republika Uczonych*, Wrocław, Oficyna Wydawnicza Atut, 2006, s. 450-471.

[56] Roman Duda, "Lwowska szkoła matematyczna" (Lvov School of Mathematics), Wrocław: Wyd. Uniwersytetu Wrocławskiego, 2007.

[57] Jarosław Górnicki, "O podziale prostokąta na kwadraty" (About Dividing a Rectangle into Squares), *Delta*, No. 7 (187), 13–15 (1989).

[58] Piotr Hajłasz (ed.), "Stefan Banach o swoim ojcu" (Stefan Banach Jr about his Father), *Delta*, No. 10 (221), 1–4 (1992).

[59] A. Gulisashwili, "Gustave Choquet rozmawia o swoim pobycie w Polsce po II wojnie światowej" (Gustave Choquet Talks about His Visit to Poland after World War II), em Wiadom. Mat. 39 (2003), 157-164.

[60] Michał Heller, *Szczęście w przestrzeniach Banacha* (Happiness in Banach Spaces) (Znak Publ., Krakow, 1995).

[61] Tadeusz Iwiński, *Ponad pół wieku działalności matematyków polskich. Zarys historii Polskiego Towarzystwa Matematycznego 1919–1973* (The Work of Polish Mathematicians Spanning More than Half a Century: An Outline of the History of the Polish Mathematical Society 1919–1973) (PWN, Warsaw, 1975).

[62] Józef Kozielecki, *Banach, geniusz ze Lwowa* (Banach, a Genius from Lvov) (Żak Akademic Publ., Warsaw, 1999).

[63] Stefan Kryński, "Rudolf Weigl (1883–1957)", e-print at http://lwow.eu/weigl/czlowiek.html

[64] Kazimierz Kuratowski, "Moje wspomnienia związane z powstaniem polskiej szkoły matematycznej" (My Recollections on the Origins of the Polish School of Mathematics), *Wiadomości Matematyczne* 12, 9–15 (1969).

[65] Kazimierz Kuratowski, *Notatki do autobiografii* (Notes to Autobiography) (Czytelnik Publ., Warsaw, 1981).

[66] Franciszek Leja, "Powstanie Polskiego Towarzystwa Matematycznego" (The Establishment of the Polish Mathematical Society), *Wiadomości Matematyczne* 12, 3–8 (1969).

[67] Edward Marczewski, "Początki matematyki wrocławskiej" (The Beginnings of the Wroclaw School of Mathematics), *Wiadomości Matematyczne*, 12, 63–76 (1969).

[68] Stanisław M. Mazur, "Przemówienie wygłoszone na uroczystości ku uczczeniu pamięci Stefana Banacha" (An Address Delivered at the Stefan Banach Memorial Conference), *Wiadomości Matematyczne* 4, 249–250 (1961).

[69] Bogdan Miś, "Opowieści Księgi Szkockiej" (Tales of the Scottish Book), *Perspektywy*, No. 12, 17–19 (1969).

[70] Władysław Narkiewicz, "Matematycy Wrocławscy 1900-1945", (Wrocław Mathematicians 1900-1945), *Wiadom. Mat.* 39 (2003), s. 107-115.

[71] Siergiej M. Nikolski, "Wspomnienie o Stefanie Banachu", (Reminiscences of Stefan Banach), *Wiadomości Matematyczne* **30** (1), 115–120 (1993).

[72] Disan Nikonowicz, "Stefan Banach (1892–1945)", *Matematyka* **45**, No. 4, 68–89 (1992).

[73] Nina Nowakowska, "Andrzej Alexiewicz: Lwów – Poznań – Matematyka" (Lvov – Poznań – Mathematics), *Obserwator Wielkopolski*, No. 6 (142) (1990).

[74] Zofia Pawlikowska-Brożek, "Stefan Banach w świetle wspomnień" (Stefan Banach in the Light of Personal Recollections), in: Proc. of 4th Polish Workshop on History of Mathematics on *Matematyka przełomu XIX i XX wieku* (Mathematics at the Turn of the 19th Century), ed. S. Fudal (Szczecin University Press, 1990), pp. 101–112; article reprinted in [62].

[75] Aleksander Pełczyński, Zbigniew Semadeni, "Uwagi o rozwoju analizy funkcjonalnej w Polsce" (Remarks on the Development of Functional Analysis in Poland), *Wiadomości Matematyczne* **12**, 83–108 (1969).

[76] Zbysław Popławski, *Dzieje Politechniki Lwowskiej 1844–1945* (History of Lvov Polytechnic 1844–1945) (Wrocław–Warsaw–Krakow, Ossolineum, 1992); *Politechnika Lwowska 1844–1945* (Lvov Polytechnic 1844–1945), ed. R. Szewalski *et al.* (Wrocław, Wrocław Polytechnic Publ., 1993).

[77] Tadeusz Riedl, *Chodząc po Lwowie* (Strolling in Lvov) (Bernardinum Publ., Pelplin, 2006).

[78] Sergei L. Sobolev, "Przemówienie wygłoszone na uroczystości ku uczczeniu pamięci Stefana Banacha", (An Address Delivered at the Stefan Banach Memorial Conference), *Wiadomości Matematyczne* **4**, 263–264 (1961).

[79] Hugo Steinhaus, *Kalejdoskop matematyczny* (Mathematical Snapshots) – enlarged edition (Wyd. Szkolne i Pedagogiczne, Warsaw 1989).

[80] Hugo Steinhaus, "Stefan Banach. Przemówienie wygłoszone na uroczystości ku uczczeniu pamięciStefana Banacha", (Stefan Banach. An Address Delivered at the Stefan Banach Memorial Conference), *Wiadomości Matematyczne* **4**, 251–259 (1961).

[81] Hugo Steinhaus, *Wspomnienia i zapiski* (Reminescencs and Notes), edited by A. Zgorzelska (Aneks Publ., London, 1992).

[82] Marshall H. Stone, "Nasz dług wobec Stefana Banacha. Przemówienie wygłoszone na uroczystości ku uczczeniu pamięci Stefana Banacha",

(Our Debt to Stefan Banach. An Address Delivered at the Stefan Banach Memorial Conference), *Wiadomości Matematyczne* **4**, 265–267 (1961).

[83] Kazimierz Szałajko, "Wspomnienia o Kole Matematyczno-Fizycznym Studentów UJK we Lwowie", (Reminiscences about the Mathematical-Physical Circle at the Jan Kazimierz University in Lvov), *Wiadomości Matematyczne* **26**, 86–88 (1984).

[84] Kazimierz Szałajko, "Wspomnienia o Stefanie Banachu na tle Lwowa i lwowskiej szkoły matematycznej", (Reminiscences of Stefan Banach Against the Background of Lvov and the Lvovian School of Mathematics), *Opuscula Mathematica* **13**, 45–54 (1993).

[85] Béla Szökefalvi-Nagy, "Przemówienie wygłoszone na uroczystości ku uczczeniu pamięci Stefana Banacha", (An Address Delivered at the Stefan Banach Memorial Conference), *Wiadomości Matematyczne* **4**, 269–270 (1961).

[86] Andrzej Turowicz, Reminiscences recorded on a tape (in Polish), Tyniec, April 27th, 1989.

[87] Stanisław Ulam, "Wspomnienia z Kawiarni Szkockiej", (Reminiscences from the Scottish Café), *Wiadomości Matematyczne* **12**, 49–58 (1969).

[88] Antoni Wiweger, "Stefan Banach", *Delta*, No. 2, 4–5 (1974).

[89] Krystyna Wuczyńska, "O podręcznikach szkolnych Stefana Banacha", (About the School Textbooks Written by Stefan Banach), *Matematyka* **45**, 96–100 (1992).

[90] — "Wyjątki z księgi protokołów Towarzystwa Matematycznego w Krakowie. Faksymile Zebrania Konstytucyjnego", (Extracts from the Protocol Book of the Mathematical Society in Krakow. Facsimile of the Meeting about the Constitution), *Wiadomości Matematyczne* **22**, 155–157 (1979).

Biographical Notes

[B-1] **Alexiewicz, Andrzej**
(b. 11 February 1917, in Lvov, d. 11 July 1995, in Poznań) – studied mathematics at the Jan Kazimierz University in Lvov under S. Banach and H. Auerbach, S. Kaczmarz, S. Mazur, W. Orlicz, J. Schauder, H. Steinhaus and E. Żyliński. He completed his studies in 1940 and worked as an assistant in Stefan Banach's Faculty of Mathematical Analysis. He was a lice feeder in Professor Weigl's Epidemic Typhus Research Institute. In May 1944, he earned a doctorate for his work "On Sequences of operations" under Professor Władysław Orlicz. From 1945 until his death he worked at Poznań University. He was a Deputy Rector at the Adam Mickiewicz University and Dean of the Mathematics, Physics and Chemistry Faculty there. Author of a monograph on *Functional Analysis* [47].

[B-2] **Alexiewicz, Władysław**
(b. 1943 in Lvov) – son of Andrzej Alexiewicz, Professor Extraordinarius at the Physics Institute of the Adam Mickiewicz University in Poznań.

[B-3] **Banach, Stefan Jr**
(b. 14 October 1922, in Lvov, d. 25 February 1999, Warsaw) – son of Stefan Banach. He was married to Alina (née Filipowicz) and had two daughters Iwona and Kasia). He was an associate professor at the Clinic of Neurosurgery of the Medical Academy in Warsaw. During WWII he was also employed as a feeder of lice in Professor Weigl's Epidemic Typhus Research Institute in Lvov.

[B-4] **Bartel, Kazimierz**
(1882–1941) – a mathematician and politician who was Prime Minister of Poland (1926–1930). During WWII the Nazis wanted him to create a Polish puppet government. After he refused he was executed on orders of Heinrich Himmler on 26 July 1941.

[B-5] Ciesielski, Krzysztof
(b. 1956) - a mathematician. He works at the Jagiellonian University, in 1999-2008 he was a vice-Head of the Mathematics Institute at this university. His main mathematical interest is topological dynamical systems. An author and co-author of more than 200 articles presenting mathematics in a popular way. He was awarded (jointly with Z.Pogoda) some prestigeous prizes, including the Great Dickstein Prize of the Polish Mathematical Society and the Steinhaus Prize from the Polish Foundation for Science Advancement. Since 1987 a member of the Editorial Board (a Correspondent) of "The Mathematical Intelligencer", since 1999 an Associate Editor of the "European Mathematical Society Newsletter".

[B-6] Czekanowski, Jan
(1882–1965) – a Polish anthropologist, statistician and linguist.

[B-7] Domoradzki, Stanisław
Graduated in mathematics at the Jagiellonian University in Krakow (1982) PhD in mathematical sciences (Higher College of Teacher Training in Krakow, 1995). Areas of scientific interest: history of mathematics, mathematics teaching. Co-author of the "Bibliographical Dictionary of Polish Mathematicians" (2003), academic teacher at the University of Rzeszów. Married to Elżbieta, two sons: Tomasz and Jakub.

[B-8] Duda, Roman
Roman Duda studied at Wroclaw University, Poland, and worked at the Mathematical Institutes of The Polish Academy of Science and of Wroclaw University. A professor at Wroclaw University he is now retired. His academic interests include topology and the history of mathematics. His other interests have been in politics (among others he has held positions as Senator of the Republic of Poland and as Vice Minister for Education), and in mathematical publications (acting as editor-in-chief of "Mathematical News" and as member of several other publication committees). He also enjoys good literature.

[B-9] Filipowicz-Banach, Alina
(b. 16 August 1926, in Sokółka) – wife of Stefan Banach Jr, Professor of Opthamology. Formerly Director of the ophthalmology ward of a major Warsaw hospital. Currently resident in Warsaw.

[B-10] Greczek, John. J
(born in Krakow, Poland) – son of Wilhelm Greczek, grandson of Stefan Greczek, nephew of Stefan Banach. He received his education in

the United Kingdom, attended Edinburgh, Glasgow and London Universities graduating with a Ph.D. in 1965. Since then he has worked as a chemical engineer with a major chemical company and a multinational oil company in plant management and operations, process design and development and process safety management. Since 1997 he has been with the USA Government with responsibility to oversee and coordinate process safety inspections conducted in refineries and chemical plants throughout the Midwest region of the USA.

[B-11] **Kałuża, Roman**

(1949–1998). Author, publicist, philosopher; he studied at the Jagiellonian University, the Krakow Academy of Economics, and at the Sorbonne. He is the author of books on science and popular science and an in-depth reporter. He has contributed articles to the New Yorker, Die Welt, Le Figaro, Stern, L'Aarche, L'Evenement, Studium Papers, FAZ, the Vienese Courier and Hamburger ART. He is also the author of the first comprehensive biography [19] of Stefan Banach published in Polish, English and Japanese.

[B-12] **Kordos, Marek**

(b. 1940) – Professor Extraordinarius at Warsaw University, since 1963 on the staff of Warsaw University, since the founding of the monthly *Delta* in 1974, its editor-in-chief. Working in the fields of non-Euclidian geometry, projective and projective-metric geometry. Since 1986 he has been lecturing on the history of mathematics at various academic institutions. The recipient of the Samuel Dickstein (1982) prize and the Hugo Steinhaus prize (1996) for popularising mathematics.

[B-13] **Musielak, Julian**

(b. 1928 in Poznań) – student of Professor Władysław Orlicz, Emeritus Professor of the Institute of Mathematics at the Adam Mickiewicz University (AMU). He was Rector of the AMU, Dean of the Mathematical-Physics Faculty and Director of the Institute of Mathematics at AMU. He founded and edited the periodical *Functiones et Approximation*, and was editor-in chief of *Commentationes Mathematicae* and co-editor of *Mathematicae Japonica*. Under his tutelage 36 students were awarded doctorates and he has written over 160 papers on functional analysis and its applications. Among others in his work he has investigated and described the properties of abstract mathematical spaces, now named *Musielak-Orlicz spaces*.

[B-14] Pawlikowska-Brożek, Zofia
MSc at the Jagiellonian University (1963), PhD in mathematical sciences at the JU, (1970) (thesis supervisor: Zdizsław Opial). Working at the AGH University of Science and Technology since 1963 (adiunkt since 1970). Specialization: history of mathematics. Over 50 publications, including: "Writing the History of Mathematics: Its Historical Development" (Birkhauser Verlag, 2002), entries in the *Polish Bibliographical Dictionary* and *The PWN Great Encyclopedia.* Co-editor of "The History of Polish Science. The 20th century. Exact Sciences" (1995) and the *Bibliographical Dictionary of Polish Mathematicians* (2003). Head of the Commission for the History of Mathematics of the Polish Mathematical Society (1978-2000). Initiated and co-organized Schools on the History of Mathematics. Co-president of the Commission for the History of Exact Sciences (Astronomy, Mathematics) of the Committee for the History of Science and Technology of the Polish Academy of Sciences (1990-2007) (still member of the Committee).

[B-15] Piłsudski, Józef
(1867–1935) – a Polish revolutionary and statesman. He is considered largely responsible for Poland having regained her independence in 1918, 123 years after she was last partitioned in 1795. From 1926 to 1935 he exercised absolute power as head of the Second Polish Republic.

[B-16] Pogoda, Zdzisław
(b. 1955 in Krakow). Graduated in mathematics from the Jagiellonian University in Krakow (1979), where he also obtained PhD degree (1982). After the studies he started working at UJ, where he is still employed. His mathematical interests are connected with differential geometry and its applications, popularization and history of mathematics especially the history of geometry and topology. He is an author (and coauthor, mainly with Krzysztof Ciesielski) of over 100 papers, four books and three handbooks. For his work to popularize mathematics he has been awarded (jointly with K. Ciesielski) the Great Dickstein Prize of the Polish Mathematical Society. He also received the Hugo Steinhaus and Hugo Kołłątaj Prizes.

[B-17] Riedl, Tadeusz
(b. 1933 in Lvov) – former Rector of the Academy of Physical Education (AWF) and Sport in Gdańsk, Director of the Department of Tourism, Recreation and Ecology and Director of the Division of General Biology and Ecology at AWF in Gdańsk. Discovered 20 hitherto

unknown invertebrates and established 6 new taxons.

[B-18] **Sowińska, Maria**

(nee Puchalska, b. 1942 in Krakow, Poland), granddaughter of Maria Puchalska. She studied at the Jagellonian University in Krakow and is an art historian. From 1968 until 1987 she worked as a curator at the Polish National Museum in Krakow. Since 1987 she has been head antiquarian in DESA, a major antiquities store in Krakow.

[B-19] **Szybalski, Wacław**

(b. 9 September 1921, in Lwów, Poland) – Polish scholar, biotechnologist and geneticist, Professor of Oncology at the University of Wisconsin, Madison, WI (USA). Professor Szybalski is the recipient of four honorary doctorates from Polish universities: UMCS in Lublin, Gdańsk University of Technology, the Gdańsk Medical Academy and Gdańsk University. He is a member of the Polish Academy of Sciences, has received numerous academic prizes and is a pioneer and world authority on multiple drug therapy, molecular genetics of viruses, gene therapy and the cloning and sequencing of human DNA. He was during the war a supervisor of a group in Professor Weigl's Epidemic Typhus Research Institute.

[B-20] **Ulam, Stanisław Marcin**

(b. 13 April 1909, in Lvov, d. 13 May 1984, in Santa Fe) – student and collaborator of Stefan Banach, one of the most renowned representatives of the Lvov School of Mathematics with major achievements in mathematics (topology, set theory, theory of measure, group theory, and others) and physics. From 1936 he worked in the USA including at the University of Colorado, Boulder, among others. Together with Edward Teller he developed the theory behind the construction of the first American hydrogen bomb. Hans Bethe called Ulam the father of the hydrogen bomb.

[B-21] **Waksmundzka-Hajnos,Monika**

(b. 1950 in Lublin) – daughter of Andrzej[B22] and Antonina née Greczek, granddaughter of Stefan Greczek, niece of Stefan Banach. Professor of pharmacology and doctor of chemistry. Since 1973 she has been at the Department of Inorganic and Analytical Chemistry of the Pharmacy Faculty of the Lublin Medical Academy, and since 2003 the Director of the Inorganic Chemistry Division of that Department.

[B-22] **Waksmundzki, Andrzej**

(1910–1998) – husband of Antonina Greczek and father of Monika

Hajnos-Waksmundzka, was a renowned Polish physical chemist, founder of the Polish School of Chromatography and a pioneer in the
technology of luminophores. He received his Ph.D. from the Jagiellonian University in Krakow. During WWII he was part of the Polish
underground resistance and, among others, responsible for the rescue and safe transport of people from Poland to Hungary. Arrested
by the Gestapo in 1942 he was imprisoned and held consecutively in
four concentration camps that included Auschwitz, Gross Rosen and
Mauthausen. From 1969 until 1976 he served on the main board of
the Polish Government's Ministry of Science and Higher Education.
He was the recipient of several Polish State Awards and three honoris
causa doctorates.

[B-23] **Weigl, Rudolf**

(1883–1957) – renowned Polish biologist and inventor of the first effective vaccine for epidemic typhus. He was called the Polish "Schindler"
and in 2003 he was awarded a medal and diploma from Yad Vashem
Institute as "The Righteous Among Nations".

[B-24] **Zarichny, Michailo**

Graduated in mathematics at the State University of Lvov (1979),
PhD at the University of Moscow (1983), habilitation at the University
of Moscow (1992), academic title of professor (Kiev, 1994), professor
of mathematics at the University of Lvov since 1994, Dean of the
Faculty of Mechanics and Mathematics in Lvov since 2004. Main
areas of scientific interest: geometric topology, topological algebra.
Interested in belles-lettres and music. Married to Lidia, children: Igor
and Sofija.

[B-25] **Żuraniewska, Alicja**

(b. 1943 in Krakow, Poland) – daughter of Tadeusz and Anna Greczek, granddaughter of Stefan Greczek, niece of Stefan Banach. She
received her LLM degree from the Jagiellonian University. She currently has a private law office in Krakow.

(Translated[1] by *John Greczek*)

---

[1]Except the note of Krzysztof Ciesielski.

List of Illustrations

Chapter 1.3 (Insert 1)

1. The old Jan Kazimierz University (JKU) at 4, St. Nicholas Street, and the St. Nicholas Church - from a 1915 postcard.
2. The old JKU - from a contemporary photograph.
3. Professor Andrzej Alexiewicz participating in the ceremony to place a medallion of Stefan Banach on the wall of a building of the old JKU, in 1992.
4. JKU as seen on a 1938 postcard.
5. JKU as seen on a 1938 postcard.
6. JKU as seen on a 1939 postcard.
7. JKU - presently the Iwan Franko University - from a contemporary photograph.
8. In this building the "Scottish Café" was located – from a contemporary photograph.
9. "Roma Café" (on the left) and the "Scottish Café" (on the right) on Fredro Place - from a 1916 postcard.
10. Inside of the "Scottish" Café - from a pre-war postcard.
11. Lvov Polytechnic - from a pre-war postcard c. 1910-1915.
12. Lvov Polytechnic - from a contemporary photograph.

The postcards are from a collection belonging to Prof. Wladyslaw Alexiewicz, used here with his permission. Photograph 2 is from a private collection of the Riedl family, used here with the permission of Prof. Tadeusz Riedl. Photograph 3 is from a private collection of the Alexiewicz family, used here with the permission of Prof. Wladyslaw Alexiewicz. Photograph is used here with the permission of Dr. Nikodem Miranowicz. Photographs 8 and 12 are used here with the permission of Mr. Stanislaw Kosiedowski.

Chapter 1.7

- Facsimile of a postcard issued on the occasion of a 1969 jubilee meeting of the Polish Mathematical Society in Krakow to commemorate its fiftieth anniversary. The choice of the image of Stefan Banach on it is emphatic witness to the recognition of his greatness. The postcard is from a collection belonging to Prof. Wladyslaw Alexiewicz.
- Facsimile of an article by Stefan Banach titled "In Remembrance of the Murdered Scholars" about Wlodzimierz Stożek and Antoni Łomnicki, Free Poland, Moscow, a weekly publication of the Association of Polish Patriots, nr.46, 18 XII 1944.
- Translation of the Stefan Banach's article "In Remembrance of the Murdered Scholars".

Insert 2

1. The 3-year-old Stefan Banach in the Planty Park in Krakow.
2. Stefan Banach at about 5 years of age.
3. Henryk Siemiradzki and Stefan Banach playing chess, c. 1898.
4. Stefan Banach with Franciszka Plowa, c. 1900.
5. Juliusz Mien (1842-1905).
6. Stefan Banach on the day of his first Holy Communion.
7. Stefan Banach during his first year in grammar school, 1902/1903.
8. Stefan Banach, aged 12, with Jozef Siemiradzki.
9. Stefan Banach (on the left) during his third year of grammar school, 1904/1905.
10. Stefan Banach during his fourth year in grammar school, 1905/1906.
11. Stefan Banach during his sixth year in grammar school, 1907/1908.
12. Stefan Banach during his seventh year in grammar school, 1908/1909.
13. Stefan Banach at 18 years of age, after receiving his grammar school diploma ("Matura"), 1910.
14. Facsimile of The Report Card, first year of grammar school.
15. Report Card, first year of grammar school (a reproduction).
16. Facsimile of The Report Card, seventh year of grammar school.
17. Report Card, first year of grammar school (a reproduction).
18. Stefan Banach at about 19 years of age.
19. Stefan Banach at about 22 years of age.

44. Statue of Stefan Banach in front of the Mathematics and Physics Institute of the Jagellonian University in Krakow.
45. Bust of Stefan Banach in the Stefan Banach International Mathematical Center in Warsaw.
46. Medallion with bust of Stefan Banach on the wall of a building of the old Jan Kazimierz University, Lvov.
47. Postage stamp with image of Stefan Banach.
48. Medal of the Polish Academy of Science to commemorate the hundredth anniversary of the birth of Stefan Banach.
49. Reverse of the Medal.

Photographs 1 through 7, 9 and 10 are taken by Juliusz Mien. Photographs 1, 2 and 4 through 11, 13 and 18 through 29, 32 and 34 through 36, 38 through 41, 44, 48 and 49 are from the private collection of the Banach family and are used here with the permission of Prof. Alina Filipowicz-Banach. Photograph 3 is from a collection of the Krakow City Museum. Photographs 4 and 12 are from the private collection of Maria Puchalska, used here with the permission of Maria Sowińska. Photographs 14 and 16 are from a collection in the National Archives in Krakow. Photographs 30, 31, 33 and 37 are from a collection of the Mathematical Institute of the Polish Academy of Science in Sopot and were provided by Prof. Zbigniew Ciesielski. Photographs 42 and 43 are from a private collection of the Riedl family and used here with the permission of Prof. Tadeusz Riedl. Photograph 45 is the property of and used here with the permission of Nikodem Miranowicz. Photograph 46 is the property of and used here with the permission of Stanislaw Kosiedowski. Photograph 47 is from the stamp collection of Prof. Władyslaw Alexiewicz.

Chapter 2

- Facsimile of the first letter of Stefan Banach to Stanislaw Ulam (pages 1, 2, 3 and 4). The letter is from a collection in the archives of the Mathematical Institute of the Polish Academy of Science and is used here with the permission of Prof. Zbigniew Ciesielski.
- Facsimile of the second letter of Stefan Banach to Stanislaw Ulam (pages 1 and 2). The letter is from a collection in the archives of the Mathematical Institute of the Polish Academy of Science and is used here with the permission of Prof. Zbigniew Ciesielski.

- Facsimile of the enclosure (pages 1 through 5) with the second letter of Stefan Banach to Stanislaw Ulam, from the library collection of the American Philosophical Society in Philadelphia.
- Facsimile of the third letter of Stefan Banach to Stanislaw Ulam (pages 1 through 4), from the library collection of the American Philosophical Society in Philadelphia.
- Facsimile of the rough draft of a letter from Stefan Greczek to Stefan Banach (page 1), from the archives of the Greczek family, made available by Mrs. Alicja Żuraniewska.

Chapter 3.2 (Insert 3)

1. Identity Card of Franciszka Plowa.
2. Obituary notice of the death of Franciszka Plowa.
3. Identity Card of Maria Puchalska.
4. Maria Puchalska.
5. Maria Puchalska.

Photographs 1, 2, 3 and 5 are from the private collection of the family of Maria Puchalska, made available by Maria Sowińska. Photograph 4 is from the private collection of the Banach family, made available by Prof. Alina Filipowicz-Banach.

Chapter 3.5 (Insert 4)

1. Józef Greczek, father of Stefan Greczek.
2. Stefan Greczek, father of Stefan Banach.
3. Stefan Greczek.
4. Stefan Greczek.
5. Identity Card of Stefan Greczek.
6. Diploma of Emperor Franz Joseph I awarded to Stefan Greczek.
7. The children of Stefan Greczek. From the left: Antonina Greczek, Wilhelm S. Greczek, Justyna Greczek (wife of Wilhelm), Tadeusz Greczek, 1935.
8. Antonina Greczek, c. 1938.
9. Wilhelm S. Greczek at about 24 years of age. Photograph taken c. 1921.

The photographs are from the archives of the Greczek family were made available by Prof. Monika Waksmundzka-Hajnos, Mrs. Alicja Żuraniewska and Dr. John Greczek.

Chapter 3.6

- Facsimiles of "Lecture Schedules for the Academic Year 1939/1940" at the Jan Kazimierz University in Lvov.

- Translation of "Lecture Schedules".

- Facsimile of two pages from Andrzej Alexiewicz's university progress report with entries by Eustachy Żylinski, Hugo Steinhaus, Herman Auerbach, Stanisław Mazur and Stefan Banach.

- Facsimile of the first page of a manuscript by Andrzej Alexiewicz with the heading *Conversations with Banach*.

These materials are from the private collection of the Alexiewicz family, made available by Władyslaw Alexiewicz.

Chapter 3.8 (Insert 5)

1. The Professors' House at 11 Supinski Street.
2. House at 22 St. Jacek Street.
3. House at 23 Zyblikiewicza Street.
4. The Riedl family house at 12 Dwiernicki Street.

These photographs are from the private collection of the Riedl family, made available by Prof. Tadeusz Riedl.

Chapter 4

- The facsimile of the cession on behalf of his wife Łucja. Document from the archival collection of the Institute of Mathematics of the Polish Academy of Sciences reproduced by kind permission of Professor Zbigniew Ciesielski.
- Translation of the cession.
- The facsimile of Stefan Banach's oath of office. Document from the Archive of the Lvov University, supplied by Professor Mikhailo Zarichny.

- Translation of the oath.
- The facsimile of Stefan Banach's nomination as a full professor. Document from the Archive of the Lvov University, supplied by Professor Mikhailo Zarichny
- Translation of the nomination.
- The facsimile of Stefan Banach's curriculum vitae (in Ukrainian) Most probably written by Miron Zarycki, signed by S. Banach.
- Translation of Stefan Banach's curriculum vitae

Chapter 6

- Figure: "Space of continuous functions".
- Figure: "Breaking a ball into finite number of pieces"
- Figure: "Decomposition of the square into 21 different squares".

Chapter 7

- Illustration to problem 152 from *Scottish Book.*
- The facsimile of the first page of the *Scottish Book.*
- The facsimile of the second page of the *Scottish Book.*

(Translated by *John Greczek*)

Index of Names

181